Table of Contents

PRESOLO KNOWLEDGE EXAM

According to FAR 61.87 Solo Requirements for Student Pilots, as a student pilot, you must demonstrate satisfactory aeronautical knowledge on an exam that evaluates your knowledge of:

- Applicable sections of FAR Parts 61 and 91.
- Airspace rules and procedures for the airport where the solo flight will be performed.
- Flight characteristics and operational limitations for the make and model of aircraft to be flown.

Your instructor must administer the exam, and at the conclusion of the exam, review all the incorrect answers with you before authorizing you to conduct a solo flight.

PRESOLO KNOWLEDGE EXAM

This exam contains a total of 50 questions — 20 general questions, 10 aircraft questions, and 20 airport and airspace questions. Normally, the general and aircraft questions apply to all students; however, some of the airport and airspace questions may not be applicable. Flight instructors who administer this test may add or delete questions as necessary to make the exam more appropriate to the training aircraft and the surrounding flight environment.

GENERAL QUESTIONS

Instructions: All students should answer the general questions.

1. What personal documents and endorsements are you required to have before you fly solo?

   _____

   _____

2. What are your student pilot limitations regarding carriage of passengers or cargo and flying for compensation or hire?

   _____

   _____

   _____

3. Explain student pilot limitations concerning visibility and flight above clouds.

   _____

   _____

   _____

4. Who has the final authority and responsibility for the operation of the airplane when you are flying solo?

   _____

   _____

5. Discuss what preflight action concerning the airport and airplane performance is specified in the regulations for a local flight.

   _____

   _____

   _____

6. During engine runup, you cause rocks, debris, and propeller blast to be directed toward another aircraft or person. Could this be considered careless or reckless operation of an aircraft?_____

7. You may not fly as pilot of a civil aircraft within ____ hours after consumption of any alcoholic beverage, or while you have ____% by weight or more alcohol in your blood.

8. What are the general requirements pertaining to the use of safety belts and shoulder harnesses?

   _____

   _____

   _____

9. What is the minimum fuel reserve for day VFR flight, and on what cruise speed is the fuel reserve based?

_____

_____

10. A transponder with Mode C/ADS-B (2020) is required at all times in all airspace at and above ____ feet MSL, excluding that airspace at and below _____ feet AGL.

11. What aircraft certificates and documents must be on board when you are flying solo?

A — _____

R — _____

R — _____

O — _____

W — _____

12. No person may operate an aircraft so close to another aircraft as to create a(n)_____.

13. Who has the right-of-way when two aircraft are on final approach to land at the same time?

_____

_____

14. What action do you need to take if you are overtaking another aircraft and which aircraft has the right-of-way? What should you do if you are flying a head-on collision course with another aircraft? If another single-engine aircraft is converging from the right, who has the right-of-way?

_____

_____

_____

15. Except when necessary for takeoffs and landings, what are the minimum safe altitudes when flying over congested and other than congested areas?

_____

_____

16. If an altimeter setting is not available at an airport, what setting should you use before departing on a local flight?

_____

_____

17. What altitudes should you use when operating under VFR in level cruising flight at more than 3,000 feet AGL?

_____

_____

PRESOLO KNOWLEDGE EXAM

18. When practicing steep turns, stalls, and maneuvering during slow flight, the entry altitude must allow a recovery to be completed no lower than _____ feet AGL.

19. When is a go-around appropriate?

_____

_____

20. What general steps should you follow after an engine failure in flight?

_____

_____

_____

AIRCRAFT QUESTIONS

Instructions: All students should answer the aircraft questions. If necessary, the instructor may include additional questions that are pertinent to the make and model airplane to be flown.

1. List the minimum equipment and instruments that must be working properly in your airplane for day VFR flight.

_____

_____

_____

2. Fill in the V-speed definitions and the corresponding speed for your training airplane.

	DEFINITION	SPEED
(V_{S0})		
(V_{S1})		
(V_X)		
(V_Y)		
(V_{FE})		
(V_A)		
(V_{NO})		
(V_{NE})		

3. What is the best glide speed for your training airplane? _____ KIAS

4. What is the maximum allowable flap setting for takeoff in your airplane? _____°

5. The total usable fuel capacity for your airplane is ___ gallons. On a standard day (sea level temperature, 59°F, altimeter 29.92 in. Hg.), the fuel consumption rate during normal (approximately 75% power) cruise is ___ gallons per hour.

6. What grade or grades of fuel can be safely used in your airplane? What are the colors of the recommended fuels? What happens to the color of the fuel if two grades are mixed?

_____

_____

_____

7. The maximum oil capacity of your airplane is ___ quarts, and the minimum oil capacity to begin a flight is ___ quarts.

8. The maximum crosswind component specified by your instructor for solo takeoffs and landings in the training airplane is ___ knots.

9. If your airplane is equipped with a carburetor, when do you use carburetor heat? What are the indications of carburetor icing?

_____

_____

_____

10. What is the takeoff and landing distance over a 50-foot obstacle for your airplane at your airport? Assume maximum certificated takeoff weight, 80°F, winds calm, and an altimeter setting of 29.52 in. Hg.

_____

_____

_____

AIRPORT AND LOCAL AIRSPACE QUESTIONS

Instructions: Flight instructors might assign only those questions that pertain to the student's airport environment and surrounding local area and may assign additional questions for a particular flying area.

1. What are the traffic patterns for each runway at your airport? What is the MSL altitude for the traffic pattern?

_____

_____

_____

2. How do you enter and exit the traffic pattern at your airport? What, if any, radio communications are required?

_____

_____

_____

3. What radio calls are recommended in the traffic pattern at an uncontrolled airport? What radio calls are required at your airport?

_____

_____

_____

4. What is the standard direction of turns in the traffic pattern? Give an example of a visual display indicating a nonstandard traffic pattern.

_____

_____

5. What is CTAF? Explain CTAF procedures at your training airport(s).

_____

_____

_____

_____

6. How can you determine if a runway is closed?

_____

_____

7. What are the typical dimensions of Class D airspace and what requirement(s) must be met prior to entry?

_____

_____

_____

8. What is the maximum speed permitted for aircraft below 10,000 feet MSL? What is the maximum speed allowed in Class B airspace? What is the maximum speed allowed in a VFR corridor through Class B airspace?

_____

_____

_____

_____

9. If you receive ATC instructions that you feel might compromise safety or will cause you to violate an FAR, what should you do?

_____

_____

_____

_____

10. What is the meaning of each of the following ATC light signals?

IN FLIGHT

Steady green — _____

Flashing green — _____

Flashing red — _____

Steady red — _____

ON THE GROUND

Flashing red — _____

Flashing green — _____

11. In addition to equipment requirements and a student pilot certificate, what other requirement(s), if any, must be met before a student pilot is authorized to fly solo within Class B airspace?

_____

_____

_____

12. Explain the general transponder equipment and use requirement(s) when operating within or near Class B airspace.

_____

_____

_____

_____

_____

PRESOLO KNOWLEDGE EXAM

7

13. Describe Class B airspace boundaries, and how they apply to an airport within that airspace. Explain how you can use navigation equipment and/or ground reference points to identify the Class B boundaries. (Draw a diagram, if necessary.)

_____

_____

_____

_____

_____

14. You have called ATC just prior to entering Class B airspace, and the controller tells you to, "Squawk 2466 and ident." Are you now allowed to enter Class B airspace without any further instructions? Explain.

_____

_____

_____

15. On a sectional chart, what does a dashed magenta line around an airport indicate?

_____

_____

_____

16. Explain the minimum visibility and ceiling requirements for VFR flight in Class D airspace.

_____

_____

17. Can a student or recreational pilot request a special VFR clearance in Class D airspace when visibility is less than three miles? Explain your answer.

_____

_____

18. You have called ATC prior to entering Class C airspace, and the controller responds with your call sign and tells you to, "Standby." Are you now allowed to enter this airspace without any further instructions? Explain.

_____

_____

19. Describe the typical dimensions of Class C airspace. Is participation in the radar service mandatory within the outer area of Class C airspace?

_____

_____

_____

20. Describe the Class C boundaries that affect your airport or a nearby airport. Explain how you can use navigation equipment and/or ground reference points to identify the Class C airspace inner core surface area and shelf area, as well as the outer area. (Draw a diagram, if necessary.)

_____

_____

_____

_____

_____

STAGE I EXAM

Discovering Aviation

Completely darken only one circle for each question on the answer form.

PILOT TRAINING

1. If a third class medical certificate was issued to a 35-year-old pilot on March 26, when will it expire?
   A. March 26, 2 years later
   B. March 26, 5 years later
   C. March 31, 5 years later

2. With respect to pilot certification, which is a category and class of aircraft?
   A. Airplane; single-engine land
   B. Restricted category; airplane
   C. Single-engine land; Cessna 172

3. With respect to the certification of aircraft, which are categories of aircraft?
   A. Landplane, seaplane
   B. Normal, utility, acrobatic
   C. Airplane, rotorcraft, glider

4. Which are currency requirements that you must meet to act as pilot in command of an airplane carrying passengers?
   A. Flight review every 24 calendar months; 3 takeoffs and landings in an aircraft of the same category and class within the preceding 90 days
   B. Flight review every 12 calendar months; 3 takeoffs and landings in an aircraft of the same category and class within the preceding 90 days
   C. Flight review every 24 calendar months; 3 takeoffs and landings in an aircraft of the same class and make and model within the preceding 90 days

5. Who has the final responsibility for the safe operation of an aircraft?
   A. Pilot in command
   B. Pilot with the highest rating
   C. Person who occupies the left seat

6. When is a flight review required?
   A. Within the past 24 calendar months to act as pilot in command if carrying passengers
   B. Within the past 24 calendar months to act as pilot in command whether flying solo or carrying passengers
   C. Within the past 60 calendar months to act as pilot in command whether flying solo or carrying passengers

AVIATION OPPORTUNITIES

7. What requirement must you meet to act as pilot in command of a high-performance airplane?
   A. Pass a flight test in that airplane from an FAA inspector.
   B. Receive ground and flight instruction from an authorized flight instructor who then endorses your logbook.
   C. Pass a knowledge test on aircraft systems and receive an endorsement in your logbook that you are competent to act as pilot in command.

8. How do the FARs define a complex airplane?
   A. An airplane with an engine of more than 200 horsepower
   B. An airplane with a normal cruise speed of more than 200 knots
   C. An airplane with retractable landing gear, flaps, and a controllable-pitch propeller (or FADEC)

INTRODUCTION TO HUMAN FACTORS

9. Select the true statement regarding single-pilot resource management (SRM) concepts.
   A. The acronym SAFETY helps you remember the elements of the takeoff and before-landing briefings.
   B. Fatigue, stress, work overload, and complacency are obstacles to maintaining situational awareness.
   C. Controlled flight into terrain (CFIT) occurs when an aircraft is flown into terrain or water after receiving a faulty clearance from air traffic control.

10. Which is required by the FARs before acting as pilot in command of an aircraft?
    A. Your blood alcohol level must be less than .04 percent.
    B. Your blood alcohol level must be less than 0.4 percent.
    C. At least 4 hours must have passed after drinking alcohol.

Airplane Systems

AIRPLANES

11. Which is an inspection required by the FARs?
    A. Annual inspection for all aircraft
    B. 100-hour inspection of the transponder
    C. Inspection every 24 calendar months of the ELT

12. Select the true statement regarding airworthiness requirements.
    A. An airspeed indicator is required by FAR 91.205 for VFR flight.
    B. Complying with airworthiness directives is required only if the aircraft is operated for hire.
    C. You may fly an airplane with an inoperative altimeter if you placard the equipment as inoperative.

THE POWERPLANT AND RELATED SYSTEMS

13. Select the true statement regarding aircraft engines.
    A. Engine power decreases when you apply carburetor heat because the flow of air in the carburetor venturi is restricted.
    B. Fuel injection system components include fuel pumps, a fuel control unit, a fuel manifold valve, and fuel discharge nozzles.
    C. The basic purpose of adjusting the fuel/air mixture at altitude is to increase the fuel flow in order to compensate for decreased air density.

14. How do you operate an engine equipped with a constant-speed propeller?
    A. Use the throttle to control engine RPM as registered on the tachometer and the mixture control to regulate the power output.
    B. Use the throttle to control power output as registered on the manifold pressure gauge and the propeller control to regulate engine RPM.
    C. Use the propeller control to regulate the power output as registered on the manifold pressure gauge and the throttle control to regulate engine RPM.

15. What is detonation?
    A. Uncontrolled combustion of fuel prior to normal ignition
    B. Fuel in the cylinders exploding instead of burning smoothly
    C. The process by which the compressed fuel/air mixture is ignited to begin the power stroke

STAGE I

16. What is the probable cause if the engine magneto switch is turned to the "OFF" position, but the engine continues to run?
    A. A broken magneto ground wire
    B. Spontaneous combustion due to an overheated engine
    C. An over-voltage condition within the magneto causing the current to arc across the open contacts

FLIGHT INSTRUMENTS

17. If the pitot tube and outside static vents become clogged, which instruments are affected?
    A. Airspeed indicator, turn coordinator, and altimeter
    B. Airspeed indicator, altimeter, and vertical speed indicator
    C. Attitude indicator, heading indicator, and turn coordinator

18. What is the definition of V_{S0}?
    A. Stalling speed or minimum takeoff safety speed
    B. Stalling speed or minimum steady flight speed in a specified configuration
    C. Stalling speed or minimum steady flight speed in the landing configuration

19. According to the markings on the accompanying airspeed indicators, what is the maximum speed with flaps fully extended?
    A. (1) 91 knots; (2) 91 knots
    B. (1) 91 knots; (2) 100 knots
    C. (1) 129 knots; (2) 91 knots

20. Assume that you land at an airport with your altimeter set to 29.92 in. Hg., forgetting to set it to the current setting of 30.00 in. Hg. What will the altimeter read if the field elevation is 2,000 feet MSL?
    A. 1,920 feet MSL
    B. 2,080 feet MSL
    C. 2,800 feet MSL

21. The turn coordinator provides a direct indication of what?
    A. Rate of turn
    B. Angle of bank
    C. Pitch attitude, as well as rates of roll and turn

22. Which V-speed represents maneuvering speed?
    A. V_A
    B. V_{LO}
    C. V_{NE}

23. Select the true statement regarding the flight instruments.
    A. The attitude indicator reflects the airplane's movement about the lateral and vertical axes.
    B. The heading indicator is a gyroscopic instrument that you must align with the magnetic compass.
    C. The vertical speed indicator uses pitot pressure to display a rate of climb or descent in feet per minute.

24. Select the true statement regarding integrated flight displays.
    A. The attitude and heading reference system (AHRS) provides attitude, heading, rate of turn, and slip/skid information.
    B. The air data computer (ADC) uses pressure and temperature inputs to determine the readings for the attitude indicator, altimeter, and vertical speed indicator.
    C. The attitude and heading reference system (AHRS) uses pressure and temperature inputs to determine the readings for the airspeed indicator, altimeter, and vertical speed indicator.

Aerodynamic Principles

FOUR FORCES OF FLIGHT

25. Select the true statement regarding the creation of lift.
    A. Lowering flaps decreases the angle of attack, which decreases lift.
    B. Increasing speed while maintaining a constant angle of attack increases drag and decreases lift.
    C. When speed decreases, you must increase the angle of attack to maintain the same amount of lift.

26. Select the true statement regarding stalls.
    A. The critical angle of attack varies with airspeed, flight attitude, and weight.
    B. For a given airplane, a stall always occurs at the same airspeed, regardless of angle-of-attack, flight attitude, or weight.
    C. For a given airplane, a stall always occurs at the same angle of attack, regardless of airspeed, flight attitude, or weight.

27. How does extending the wing flaps affect lift and drag?
    A. Increases both lift and drag
    B. Increases lift and decreases drag
    C. Decreases lift and increases drag

28. What are three forms of parasite drag?
    A. Skin friction drag, induced drag, and applied drag
    B. Form drag, interference drag, and skin friction drag
    C. Interference drag, effective drag, and component drag

29. What is a result of ground effect?
    A. An increase in wingtip vortices causes a decrease in lift near the runway.
    B. The amount of thrust required to produce lift is reduced so the airplane is capable of lifting off at a lower-than-normal speed.
    C. Within one wingspan above the ground, the increase in induced drag causes the airplane to settle to the surface abruptly during landing.

STABILITY

30. What is an undesirable flight characteristic of an airplane with a CG located aft of the limit?
    A. A longer takeoff run
    B. Stalling at a higher-than-normal airspeed
    C. Difficulty in recovering from a stalled condition

31. Dihedral is used to stabilize the airplane about what axis?
    A. Lateral axis
    B. Vertical axis
    C. Longitudinal axis

32. Select the true statement regarding spins.
    A. Both wings are stalled in a spin.
    B. In a spin to the left, only the left wing is stalled.
    C. The first step of spin recovery is to add power to prevent excessive altitude loss.

AERODYNAMICS OF MANEUVERING FLIGHT

33. What is P-factor?
    A. A left-turning tendency that is most apparent at low power settings with a low angle of attack
    B. Asymmetrical thrust caused by a higher angle of attack on the left descending propeller blade, which causes an airplane to yaw to the right
    C. Asymmetrical thrust caused by a higher angle of attack on the right descending propeller blade, which causes an airplane to yaw to the left

34. What is the primary force that causes an airplane to turn?
    A. Centrifugal force
    B. Vertical component of lift
    C. Horizontal component of lift

35. Select the true statement regarding load factor.
    A. Changes in load factor occur only in turbulence.
    B. An airplane in cruising flight, while not accelerating in any direction, has a load factor of 2Gs.
    C. Load factor is the ratio of the load supported by the airplane's wings to the actual weight of the airplane.

STAGE I

The Flight Environment

SAFETY OF FLIGHT

36. What is the recommended method of scanning for other aircraft during the day?
    A. Off-center viewing and peripheral vision by scanning small sectors
    B. Regularly spaced concentration on the 3-, 9-, and 12-o'clock positions
    C. A series of short, regularly spaced eye movements to search each 10° sector of the viewing area

37. What is the most practical way to compensate for blind spots in aircraft design while climbing or descending?
    A. 360° turns
    B. Shallow S-turns
    C. 90° clearing turns

38. While heading north, you find that you are on a converging course with another airplane headed west at the same altitude. What action should you take?
    A. Remain on course, since you have the right-of-way
    B. Alter course to the left, to pass behind the other airplane
    C. Alter course to the right, to pass behind the other airplane

39. Except when necessary for takeoff and landing, when you fly over congested areas, you must maintain at least what minimum safe altitude?
    A. 1,000 feet above any obstacle
    B. 500 feet vertically and horizontally from the nearest obstacle
    C. 1,000 feet above the highest obstacle within a horizontal distance of 2,000 feet of the aircraft

40. Select the true statement regarding the effect of wind during taxi.
    A. If the wind is blowing from the left front quarter, you should turn the control wheel/stick to the right.
    B. The most critical situation exists when you are taxiing a high-wing tricycle-gear airplane in a strong quartering tailwind.
    C. A tailwheel airplane has a reduced tendency to weathervane into the wind due to the greater surface area behind the main gear.

41. Your instructor is going to demonstrate a maneuver. What is the proper procedure to transfer control of the airplane to another pilot?
    A. Tell the pilot, "You have the flight controls," and release the control stick. Visually confirm that the pilot has the control stick.
    B. Release the control stick, point to the other pilot's control stick, and say, "You have the airplane." Visually confirm that the other pilot actually takes the control stick.
    C. Tell the pilot, "You have the flight controls," continue flying until the pilot says, "I have the flight controls," and then repeat, "You have the flight controls," while visually confirming that the pilot has the flight controls.

AIRPORTS

42. Refer to the illustration and determine the appropriate landing runway and traffic pattern direction.
    A. Runway 18, left-hand traffic
    B. Runway 18, right-hand traffic
    C. Runway 36, right-hand traffic

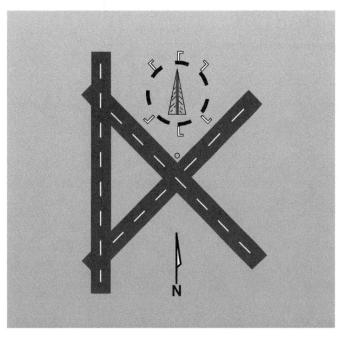

43. What is the purpose of a displaced threshold?
    A. To direct pilots to land their aircraft farther down the runway
    B. To ensure that aircraft clear the threshold lights before touching down
    C. To direct pilots to land their aircraft in full view of the control tower personnel

44. What does a large letter "X" placed near the runway threshold indicate?
    A. The airport is closed.
    B. The runway is closed.
    C. The threshold is displaced.

45. Select the true statement regarding the airport beacon.
    A. Airport beacons that indicate civilian land airports use alternating white and green lights.
    B. Two flashes of white that alternate with a single green flash indicates a heliport.
    C. The beacon operates during the day when the ceiling is less than 3,000 feet and/or the visibility is less than 5 statute miles.

46. When using two-bar VASI lights, what will you see when you are on the proper glide slope?
    A. Near bar red, far bar white
    B. Near bar white, far bar red
    C. Near bar green, far bar red

47. You accept a LAHSO clearance but on short final you experience wind shear. Your approach becomes unstable and you are uncertain that you can land and stop before the intersecting runway. What should you do?
    A. Go around, inform ATC immediately, and maneuver to avoid any conflicting traffic.
    B. Adhere to your LAHSO clearance—land and apply maximum braking effort to try to stop before the hold-short point.
    C. Land using the full runway length and advise ATC before rolling through the hold-short intersection.

STAGE I

48. Which is an example of a best practice to keep airports and aircraft secure?
    A. When you obtain a quart of oil from the FBO, you leave the keys out of sight in the airplane map/glove box.
    B. You see an individual breaking into an aircraft. You contact the flight school manager to explain the situation.
    C. You call 1-866-GA-Secure and the nearby FBO manager to report someone who appears to be attempting to open the doors of multiple aircraft.

AERONAUTICAL CHARTS

Use the chart excerpt to answer questions 49 through 53.

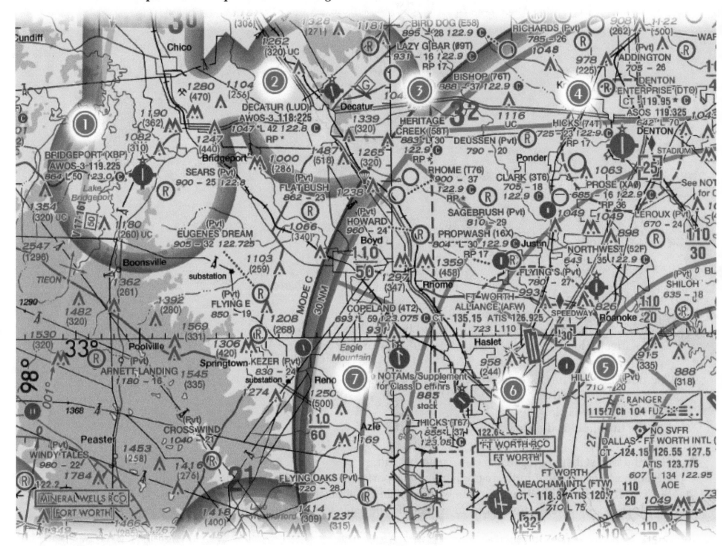

49. What is the approximate latitude and longitude of Bridgeport Airport (XBP)? (1)
    A. 32°49′N — 97°50′W
    B. 33°11′N — 97°50′W
    C. 33°11′N — 98°10′W

50. What is true about Decatur Airport? (2)
    A. The elevation is 4200 feet MSL.
    B. The airport has a control tower.
    C. Fuel and services are available during normal business hours.

51. Select the true statement regarding the communication and navigation frequencies.
    A. You can contact Heritage Creek UNICOM on 122.9. (3)
    B. The control tower at Denton Enterprise Airport does not operate continuously. (4)
    C. The line below 115.7 (Ranger VORTAC) indicates that voice communication is available on this frequency. (5)

AIRSPACE

52. What is the minimum ceiling requirement for VFR operations when operating in the traffic pattern at Ft Worth Alliance Airport? (6)
    A. 1,000 feet
    B. 1,500 feet
    C. Clear of clouds

53. What are the entry and equipment requirements to fly at 8,500 feet MSL in the airspace at position 7?
    A. Establish radio communication
    B. ATC clearance; Mode C transponder/ADS-B (2020)
    C. Establish radio communication; Mode C transponder/ADS-B (2020)

54. What action, if any, is required when you are departing a nontowered satellite airport located within Class D airspace?
    A. Contact the controlling tower as soon as practicable after takeoff.
    B. Obtain a clearance from the controlling tower by phone or radio prior to departure.
    C. After takeoff, monitor the controlling tower's frequency and proceed out of Class D airspace as soon as practicable.

55. What are your cloud clearance and visibility requirements if you obtain a special VFR clearance to operate in Class B, C, D, or E airspace that extends to the surface?
    A. Clear of the clouds; 1 SM
    B. Clear of the clouds; 3 SM
    C. 500 feet below, 1,000 feet above, and 2,000 feet horizontally; 3 SM

56. Under what condition, if any, can you fly through a restricted area?
    A. Regulations do not allow this.
    B. With authorization from the controlling agency.
    C. When flying on airways with an ATC clearance.

57. Select the true statement regarding TFRs.
    A. Compliance with TFRs is optional.
    B. TFRs are issued in NOTAMs that specify the dimensions, restrictions, and effective times.
    C. TFRs are regulatory actions that permanently restrict certain aircraft from operating within a defined area in order to protect persons or property in the air or on the ground.

58. A military aircraft appears on your left side, rocks its wings, and begins a slow left turn away from your flight path. What does this mean?
    A. You have been intercepted. Rock your wings, squawk 7700, and divert to the nearest airport.
    B. You have been intercepted. Rock your wings, turn left to follow the aircraft, squawk 7700, and attempt to contact the aircraft on 121.5 MHz.
    C. You are free to proceed on your route. The military aircraft has identified your airplane and turned away because you are not considered a threat.

STAGE I

Communication and Flight Information

ATC SERVICES

59. When ATC verifies that you are in radar contact, who is primarily responsible for VFR aircraft separation?
    A. Controller
    B. Pilot in command
    C. The controller in terminal areas and the pilot when enroute

60. Select the true statement regarding ADS-B.
    A. The ADS-B system has an effective range of 250 nautical miles.
    B. To use the ADS-B system, the airplane must have a Mode C transponder and a dedicated traffic display.
    C. ADS-B Out transmits line-of-sight signals from aircraft to ATC ground receivers and to aircraft receivers.

61. What is the correct transponder code to use for a communication failure?
    A. 7500
    B. 7600
    C. 7700

62. A controller may issue a safety alert to an aircraft in which situation?
    A. Near an area with severe thunderstorms
    B. About to enter an alert area or other special use airspace
    C. In unsafe proximity to terrain, obstructions, or other aircraft

63. You are on a heading of 270°. ATC issues this traffic advisory, *"Traffic one o'clock, two miles, southbound."* Where should you look?
    A. Southwest—between directly ahead and 90° to the left
    B. Northwest—between directly ahead and 90° to the right
    C. Southwest—between directly ahead and 90° to the right

RADIO PROCEDURES

64. What procedure applies when approaching an airport with an operating control tower?
    A. Obtain a clearance and discrete transponder code prior to entering Class D airspace.
    B. Establish two-way radio communication with the tower prior to entering Class D airspace.
    C. Establish two-way radio communication with the tower prior to entering Class E airspace.

65. What is the VHF emergency frequency monitored by most aviation ground facilities?
    A. 121.5 MHz
    B. 122.2 MHz
    C. 123.0 MHz

66. What is indicated when you use the words "PAN-PAN" in a radio message?
    A. Either an urgent or a distress condition requiring immediate assistance.
    B. A distress condition that requires immediate radio silence and assistance.
    C. An urgent situation requiring priority on the radio frequency and timely, but not immediate, assistance.

SOURCES OF FLIGHT INFORMATION

67. What frequency should you use to announce your position during an approach for a landing at Taos Municipal?
    A. 117.6 MHz
    B. 122.1 MHz
    C. 122.8 MHz

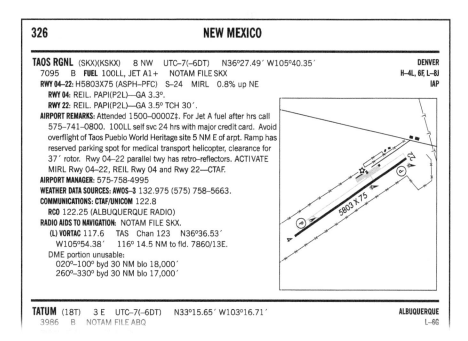

68. What is the length of the longest runway at Portland International Airport?
    A. 4,049 feet
    B. 6,600 feet
    C. 11,000 feet

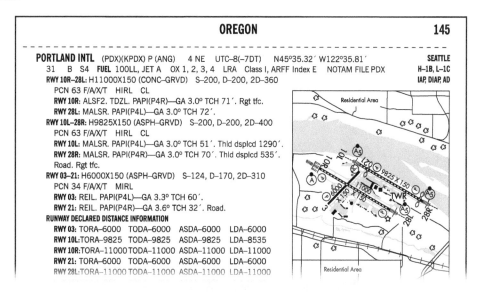

STAGE I

69. Select the true statement regarding NOTAMs.
    A. The Notices to Airmen Publication (NTAP) is issued annually and contains NOTAM(D) and FDC NOTAMs of a permanent nature.
    B. You can obtain NOTAMs from Flight Service with your online weather briefing or during a phone briefing, or use an FAA tool to search for NOTAMs online.
    C. NOTAMs include airport data that cannot be readily depicted in graphic form on charts, such as the types of runway lighting, the availability of airport services, and whether land-and-hold short operations (LAHSO) apply.

70. What information is provided by advisory circulars (ACs)?
    A. The official text of the regulations that apply to flight operations
    B. Nonregulatory information, including guidance on methods to comply with FARs
    C. Time-critical flight planning information regarding a facility, service, procedure, or hazard

STAGE II EXAM

Meteorology for Pilots

Completely darken only one circle for each question on the answer form.

BASIC WEATHER THEORY

1. What is the major motivating force behind atmospheric circulation?
   A. Rotation of the earth
   B. High and low pressure belts
   C. Uneven heating of the earth's surface

WEATHER PATTERNS

2. What processes result in moisture being added to unsaturated air?
   A. Evaporation and sublimation
   B. Condensation and sublimation
   C. Condensation and latent heat of vaporization

3. What weather conditions can you expect with a small or converging temperature/dewpoint spread?
   A. Fog and low clouds
   B. Strong surface winds
   C. Low visibility and gusty winds

4. With the approach and passage of a frontal system in the United States, what pressure and wind direction changes take place?
   A. The pressure falls as the front approaches and rises after its passage, while the wind direction shifts to the left after frontal passage.
   B. The pressure rises as the front approaches and falls after its passage, while the wind direction shifts to the left after frontal passage.
   C. The pressure falls as the front approaches and rises after its passage, while the wind direction shifts to the right after frontal passage.

WEATHER HAZARDS

5. What conditions are necessary for the formation of thunderstorms?
   A. Unstable air, a lifting force, and high moisture levels
   B. High wind velocities aloft and a small temperature/dewpoint spread
   C. The close proximity of a high pressure system to a steep pressure gradient

6. Thunderstorms and squall lines are generally associated with what type of front?
   A. Stationary
   B. Fast-moving cold
   C. Slow-moving cold

7. Select the true statement regarding wind shear.
   A. Wind shear is a sudden, drastic shift in wind speed that occurs in a horizontal plane below 1,000 feet AGL.
   B. A wind shear alert is usually issued if a reading from a LLWAS sensor differs from the mean by 5 knots.
   C. A microburst—one of the most dangerous sources of wind shear—is a downdraft associated with convective activity.

Interpreting Weather Data

THE FORECASTING PROCESS

Section A — The Forecasting Process contains content that provides a foundation for interpreting weather data.

PRINTED REPORTS AND FORECASTS

8. The elevation at Denver (KDEN) is 5,400 feet. According to the accompanying aviation routine weather report (METAR), how far below the ceiling will you be if you are flying at 7,500 feet MSL over Denver?
   A. 900 feet
   B. 2,100 feet
   C. 8,400 feet

> METAR KDEN 081055Z 21010G27KT 4SM
> —RA BR SCT015 BKN030 20/16 A2989

9. According to the accompanying terminal aerodrome forecast (TAF), what visibility and ceiling are forecast by 0500Z at KPHL?
   A. Six statute miles and 2,000 broken
   B. Four statute miles and 4,000 overcast
   C. Greater than six statute miles and a few clouds at 2,000 feet

> TAF
> KPHL 091730Z 091818 15005KT P6SM FEW020
> FM0500 27008KT 4SM OVC040 BECMG 1315
> P6SM NSW SKC=

10. Use the accompanying winds and temperatures aloft forecasts to determine the forecast wind direction, velocity and air temperature at 9,000 feet MSL over Glasgow (GGW).
    A. 310° true at 11 knots; −8°C
    B. 311° true at 10 knots; 8°C
    C. 310° magnetic at 11 knots; −8°F

	3000	6000	9000	12000	18000	24000	30000	34000	39000
GFK	0105	2809+01	2724-05	2738-10	2758-25	2776-39	279049	278552	276450
GGW		0209-02	3111-08	2923-12	2824-28	2858-39	277150	276452	274751

GRAPHIC WEATHER PRODUCTS

11. According to the low-level significant weather prognostic chart, what weather is forecast for the southeastern portion of the United States?
    A. Moderate or greater turbulence below 12,000 feet MSL
    B. A freezing level at 8,000 feet MSL and VFR conditions at the surface
    C. Ceilings below 3,000 feet and visibility below 5 miles, with IFR conditions in several states

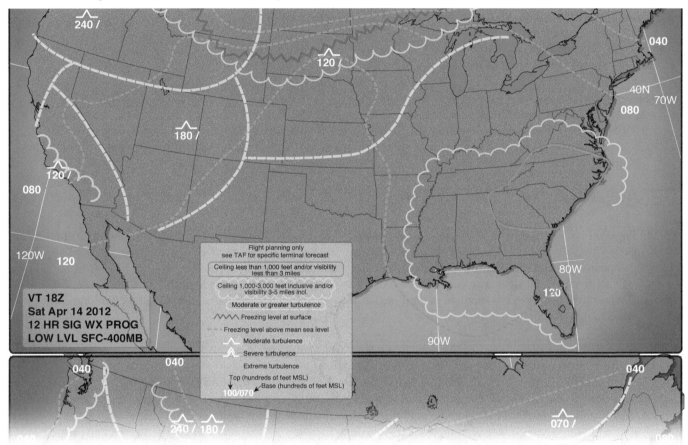

12. To what altitude is the U.S. low-level significant weather prog chart valid?
    A. 12,000 feet
    B. 18,000 feet
    C. 24,000 feet

13. What weather data can you obtain from a surface analysis chart?
    A. Areas of VFR, IFR, and MVFR conditions
    B. The location of fronts and pressure systems
    C. Forecast surface winds and temperatures at selected reporting stations

SOURCES OF WEATHER INFORMATION

14. If the departure time for your flight is six or more hours away, what type of weather briefing is appropriate?
    A. Outlook briefing
    B. Standard briefing
    C. Abbreviated briefing

15. Select the true statement regarding aviation weather sources.
    A. A center weather advisory (CWA) is a scheduled alert issued by tower controllers to warn pilots of adverse weather.
    B. Call Flight Service for a phone briefing for your specific flight at 1-800-WX-BRIEF or obtain an online weather briefing at 1800wxbrief.com.
    C. TIBS is a briefing tool that provides adverse conditions, current conditions, enroute and destination forecasts, and winds aloft for a route of flight.

16. What information should you provide to a Flight Service weather briefer?
    A. Your full name and address
    B. Whether the flight is VFR or IFR
    C. A summary of your qualifications

17. Select the true statement regarding data link weather.
    A. Data link weather services provide information on METARs and TAFs only.
    B. Data link weather services are often included with GPS and EFB cockpit or tablet display systems.
    C. The weather information displayed using a data link is real-time and should be thought of as instantaneous, up-to-date information.

FEDERAL AVIATION REGULATIONS

18. Under what circumstances is a private pilot permitted to carry a passenger who is clearly under the influence of drugs?
    A. A passenger under the influence of drugs may be carried in an emergency.
    B. Carrying any passenger who is intoxicated or under the influence of drugs is prohibited.
    C. When the passenger is a medical patient under proper care, and the pilot carries a logbook endorsement for the transportation of medical patients.

19. What preflight activities are required by the FARs for a cross-country flight?
    A. Filling out a navigation log and filing a VFR flight plan
    B. Notifying ATC of your route of flight and obtaining a transponder code for flight following
    C. Reviewing the information concerning that flight, including weather reports and forecasts, fuel and runway requirements, and alternatives available if you cannot complete the planned flight

20. As pilot in command, what action must you take with regard to safety belts?
    A. Brief all passengers on how to fasten and unfasten their safety belts and shoulder harnesses.
    B. Ensure that each passenger under the age of two is secured in an FAA-approved child safety seat during the flight.
    C. Ensure that passengers wear safety belts from the time the airplane first moves for the purpose of flight until it stops.

21. What action should you take if you receive a clearance that will cause you to deviate from an FAR?
    A. Refuse the clearance, and request an amended clearance.
    B. Accept the clearance, because ATC has assumed responsibility for the deviation.
    C. Accept the clearance, but do not comply with the portion of the clearance that would cause you to violate a regulation.

22. Which items are required to be in the airplane?
    A. Airworthiness certificate, registration certificate, and title of ownership
    B. Airworthiness certificate, registration certificate, and operating limitations
    C. Airworthiness certificate, registration certificate, and aircraft and engine logbooks

23. You may *not* operate an aircraft in aerobatic flight under what circumstances?
    A. When the flight visibility is less than 5 statute miles
    B. Over any congested area of a city, town, or settlement
    C. Within 10 nautical miles of the centerline of any Federal airway

24. According to NTSB Part 830, which of the following occurrences would require immediate notification of the NTSB?
    A. A near miss
    B. Damage in excess of $25,000 to property other than the aircraft
    C. Injury to any person or property, regardless of the extent involved

25. According to NTSB Part 830, when is the operator of an aircraft required to notify the NTSB?
    A. When the damage to an airplane exceeds $300
    B. If an aircraft experiences a flight control system malfunction or failure
    C. When an aircraft is involved in any incident, regardless of the damage received

STAGE II

STAGE II

STAGE III EXAM

Airplane Performance

Completely darken only one circle for each question on the answer form.

PREDICTING PERFORMANCE

1. What combination of conditions is most detrimental to takeoff and climb performance?
   A. Dry air and low density altitude
   B. Low temperature, low humidity, and low altitude
   C. High temperature, high humidity, and high altitude

2. Which statement is true regarding V_x?
   A. V_x is the best rate-of climb speed.
   B. V_x gives the maximum altitude gain in the least amount of time.
   C. V_x is normally used for obstacle clearance immediately after takeoff.

3. According to the accompanying chart, what is the approximate density altitude with a pressure altitude of 5,000 feet and a temperature of +40°C?
   A. 5,000 feet
   B. 8,900 feet
   C. 9,500 feet

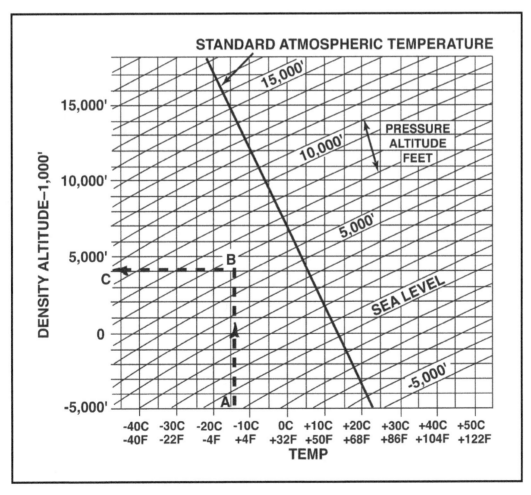

4. According to the accompanying takeoff distance chart and the following conditions, what is the total distance necessary to clear a 50-foot obstacle?

Weight ....1,670 lb

Pressure altitude ....4,000 feet

Temperature ....25° C

Headwind ....18 knots

   A. 1,664 feet

   B. 1,732 feet

   C. 2,165 feet

TAKEOFF DISTANCE

SHORT FIELD

CONDITIONS:
Flaps 10
Full Throttle Prior to Brake Release
Paved, Level, Dry Runway
Zero Wind

NOTES:
1. Decrease distances 10% for each 9 knots headwind. For operation with tailwinds up to 10 knots, increase distances by 10% for each 2 knots.
2. For operation on a dry, grass runway, increase distances by 15% of the "ground roll" figure.

WEIGHT LBS	TAKEOFF SPEED KIAS		PRESS ALT FT	0C		10C		20C		30C		40C	
	LIFT OFF	AT 50 FT		GRND ROLL	TOTAL TO CLEAR 50 FT OBS	GRND ROLL	TOTAL TO CLEAR 50 FT OBS	GRND ROLL	TOTAL TO CLEAR 50 FT OBS	GRND ROLL	TOTAL TO CLEAR 50 FT OBS	GRND ROLL	TOTAL TO CLEAR 50 FT OBS
1670	50	54	S.L.	640	1190	695	1290	755	1390	810	1495	875	1605
			1000	705	1310	765	1420	825	1530	890	1645	960	1770
			2000	775	1445	840	1565	910	1690	980	1820	1055	1960
			3000	855	1600	925	1730	1000	1870	1080	2020	1165	2185
			4000	940	1775	1020	1920	1100	2080	1190	2250	1285	2440
			5000	1040	1970	1125	2140	1215	2320	1315	2525	1420	2750
			6000	1145	2200	1245	2395	1345	2610	1455	2855	1570	3125
			7000	1270	2470	1375	2705	1490	2960	1615	3255	1745	3590
			8000	1405	2800	1525	3080	1655	3395	1795	3765	1940	4195

5. Using the listed conditions and the accompanying landing distance chart, determine the distance required to land over a 50-foot barrier.

    Pressure altitude..5,000 feet

    Temperature...15°C

    Headwind component....................................5 knots

    A. 1,470 feet

    B. 1,510 feet

    C. 1,580 feet

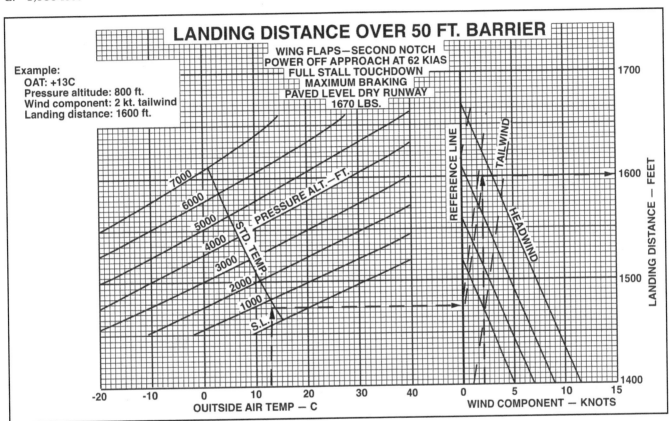

LANDING DISTANCE OVER 50 FT. BARRIER

WING FLAPS—SECOND NOTCH
POWER OFF APPROACH AT 62 KIAS
FULL STALL TOUCHDOWN
MAXIMUM BRAKING
PAVED LEVEL DRY RUNWAY
1670 LBS.

Example:
OAT: +13C
Pressure altitude: 800 ft.
Wind component: 2 kt. tailwind
Landing distance: 1600 ft.

6. Use the accompanying maximum rate-of-climb chart and the listed conditions to determine the rate of climb.

    Weight..1,670 lb

    Pressure altitude..Sea level

    Temperature...0°C

    Indicated airspeed...67 knots

    A. 742 ft/min

    B. 765 ft/min

    C. 877 ft/min

RATE OF CLIMB

CONDITIONS:
Flaps Up
Full Throttle

MAXIMUM

NOTE:
Mixture leaned above 3000 feet for maximum rpm.

WEIGHT LBS	PRESS ALT FT	CLIMB SPEED KIAS	RATE OF CLIMB — FPM			
			-20C	0C	20C	40C
1670	S.L.	67	835	765	700	630
	2000	66	735	670	600	535

STAGE III

3

7. What is the difference between the range and the endurance of an aircraft?
   A. Range is the amount of fuel required to fly to a destination, and endurance is the time it will take to get there.
   B. Range is the amount of time that the aircraft can remain in the air, and endurance is the recommended time that the pilot can fly.
   C. With a given amount of fuel, range is the distance that the aircraft can fly, and endurance is the amount of time that the aircraft can remain in the air.

WEIGHT AND BALANCE

8. What is the center of gravity (CG) of an aircraft?
   A. Location from which all horizontal measurements are made
   B. Theoretical point where all of the aircraft's lift is considered to be concentrated
   C. Theoretical point where all of the aircraft's weight is considered to be concentrated

9. Which is an item that is included in an airplane's basic empty weight?
   A. Baggage
   B. Usable fuel
   C. Unusable fuel

Use the accompanying weight and balance form to answer questions 10, 11, and 12.

WEIGHT and BALANCE			
ITEM	WEIGHT (pounds)	ARM (inches)	MOMENT (pound-inches)
Basic Empty Wt.	1772.4	+34	60,261.6
Pilot	180.0	+36	6,480.0
Front Seat Passenger	165.0	+36	5,940.0
Rear Seat Passenger	345.0	+70	24,150.0
Fuel (60 gallons)		+48	
Baggage	120.0	+95	11,400.0
TOTAL			

CG = _____ INCHES

10. What is the CG location after the airplane is loaded with full fuel?
    A. 42.16 inches
    B. 42.66 inches
    C. 43.03 inches

11. How much fuel can be carried in the airplane without exceeding a maximum takeoff weight of 2,700 pounds?
    A. 11.7 gallons
    B. 19.6 gallons
    C. 27.5 gallons

12. With the airplane in the previous problem fueled to a takeoff weight of 2,700 pounds, what is the total moment?
    A. 108,231.6 pound-inches
    B. 113,876.4 pound-inches
    C. 114,860.0 pound-inches

13. Assume an airplane has a total weight of 2,950 pounds and a total moment of 240,700 pound-inches. If the CG range is from 82.1 to 86.7 inches, what action, if any, should you take before you fly the airplane?
    A. Move some load aft in the airplane.
    B. Remove some load from the aft of the airplane.
    C. Take no action, since the airplane is properly loaded.

STAGE III

Use the loading graph and the center of gravity moment envelope graph to answer questions 14 and 15.

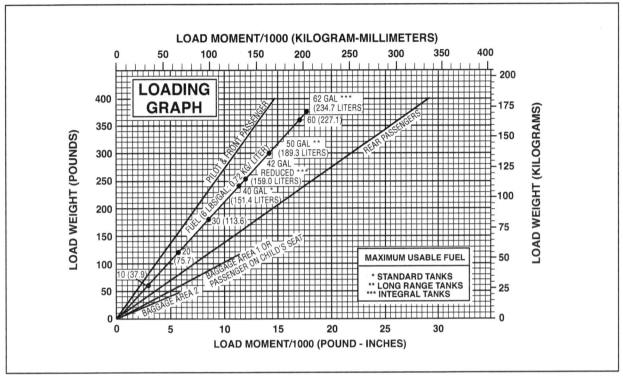

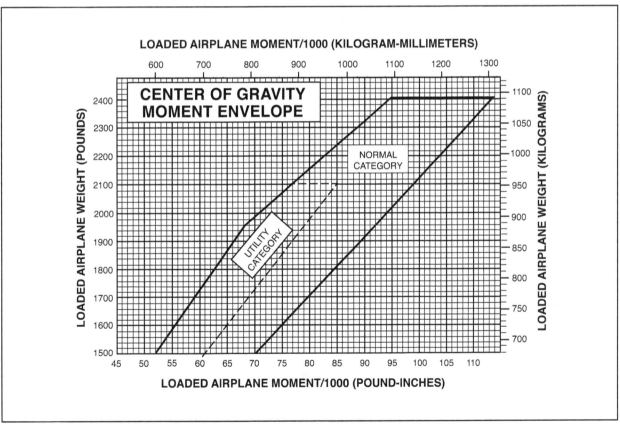

14. Based on the following conditions, what is the total moment/1000 pound-inches?

	WEIGHT	MOMENT/1000
	(lb)	(lb-inches)
Empty airplane	1,467	57.3
Pilot and front passenger	300	
Rear seat passenger	100	
Baggage area 1	100	
Fuel (40 gallons)		

    A. 40.4
    B. 47.6
    C. 96.8

15. According to the center of gravity moment envelope, where is the airplane's CG located?
    A. Out of limits, aft
    B. Within both normal and utility category limits
    C. Within normal category limits but outside utility category limits

FLIGHT COMPUTERS

16. You can use the time-speed-distance function of your flight computer to solve for what values?
    A. Groundspeed and fuel consumption
    B. Estimated time enroute and indicated airspeed
    C. Calibrated airspeed, groundspeed, and wind correction angle

17. If your airplane's fuel consumption rate is 5.6 gal/hr, how much fuel will it use on a flight of 230 NM with an average groundspeed of 93 knots?
    A. 11.3 gallons
    B. 12.5 gallons
    C. 13.8 gallons

18. Determine the density altitude using the listed conditions.

Field elevation...1,400 feet

Pressure altitude...1,500 feet

Temperature..95°F

Altimeter setting....................................29.82 inches Hg

    A. 1,300 feet
    B. 3,075 feet
    C. 4,097 feet

19. When you are flying an airplane into a left-quartering headwind, what is the effect on groundspeed and wind correction angle if the wind velocity increases?
    A. Both increase
    B. Both decrease
    C. Groundspeed decreases, and wind correction increases

STAGE III

20. If you plan to save 30 minutes fuel for reserve, how far can you fly based on the listed conditions?

    True course...175°

    Wind..030°/20 knots

    Pressure altitude...7,500 feet

    Temperature..–10°C

    Fuel consumption....................................9.5 gal/hr

    Calibrated airspeed.................................103 knots

    Fuel on board..53 gallons

    A. 655 miles
    B. 690 miles
    C. 720 miles

21. Compute the true heading and groundspeed for a cross-country flight based on the listed conditions.

    Wind..140°/25 knots

    True course...195°

    True airspeed...122 knots

    Temperature..2°C

    Pressure altitude...5,000 feet

    A. 185° and 106 knots
    B. 205° and 135 knots
    C. 186° and 138 knots

Use the following cross-country planning conditions to answer questions 22 and 23.

    Pressure altitude...7,500 feet

    Winds..280°/20 knots

    Temperature..5°C

    Calibrated airspeed.................................100 knots

    True course...050°

    Variation...13°E

    Deviation...+1°

    Fuel consumption....................................9.5 gal/hr

    Usable fuel capacity.................................36 gallons

    Distance...313 NM

22. What is the compass heading for the trip?
    A. 030°
    B. 038°
    C. 056°

23. Assuming a constant fuel consumption rate throughout the flight, how much fuel will remain after landing at the destination?
    A. 11.0 gallons
    B. 12.2 gallons
    C. 13.1 gallons

STAGE III

Navigation

PILOTAGE AND DEAD RECKONING

Use the sectional chart excerpt to answer questions 24 and 25.

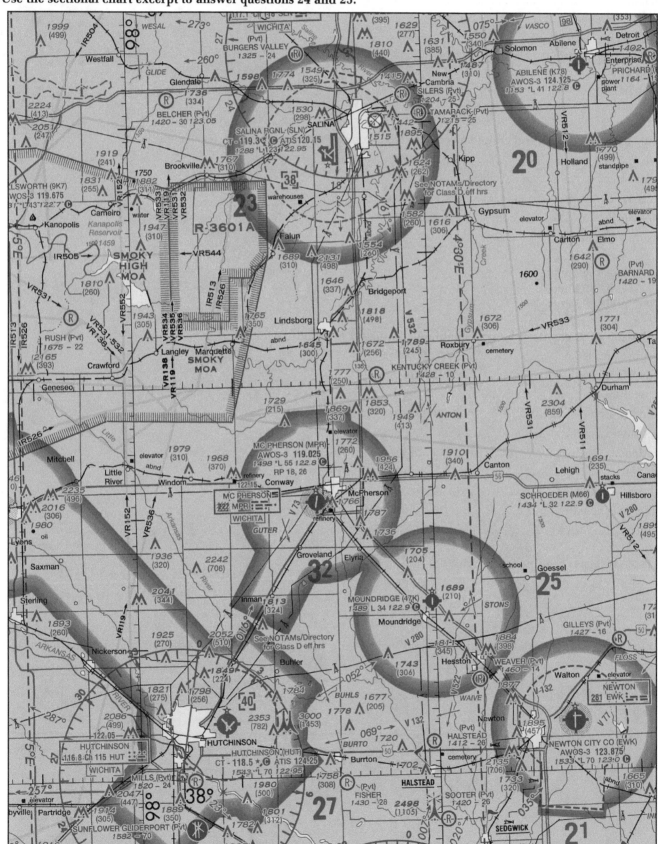

24. On a flight from Salina, on the upper portion of the chart, to Hutchinson, on the lower portion, what is your true course?
    A. 103°.
    B. 193°.
    C. 283°.

25. Assume that you are flying direct from the departure airport to the destination and the winds aloft are the same along your entire route of flight. Use the partially completed navigation log to determine the time required to fly the distance from the bridge to the destination.

Check Points (Fixes)	VOR Ident	Course (Route)	Altitude	Wind Dir.	Vel.	CAS	TC	TH	MH	CH	Dist. Leg	GS Est.	Time Off	GPH
	Freq.			Temp.	TAS		-L +R WCA	-E +W Var	±Dev		Rem.	Act.	ETE / ETA	Fuel
					125								1506Z	
											180		ATE / ATA	Rem.
KSPW				050°	15	138	355°		-1		30			
BRIDGE			6,500	5°C				11°W						

    A. 1 hour, 5 minutes
    B. 1 hour, 10 minutes
    C. 1 hour, 17 minutes

26. How do you convert true heading to magnetic heading?
    A. Add or subtract the appropriate deviation listed on the compass correction card.
    B. Compute the wind correction angle and add it to or subtract it from the true heading.
    C. Subtract easterly or add westerly variation, determined from the isogonic lines on the chart.

27. Your magnetic course is 280°. Which altitude is appropriate to meet the VFR cruising altitude requirement above 3,000 feet AGL?
    A. 5,500 feet AGL
    B. 6,000 feet MSL
    C. 6,500 feet MSL

28. For a night VFR cross-country flight, you are required to carry enough fuel to fly to the first point of intended landing and after that for what time period?
    A. 30 minutes
    B. 45 minutes
    C. 60 minutes

29. Select the true statement regarding flight plan filing.
    A. Filing a flight plan is a requirement for flights under VFR and IFR.
    B. You can file either a Domestic or ICAO flight plan for your VFR flight at 1800wxbrief.com.
    C. When using an EFB for flight plan filing, the flight plan will automatically be closed upon arrival at your destination airport.

30. Select the true statement regarding activating a flight plan.
    A. After you activate your flight plan, contact ATC enroute to update your ETE, if applicable.
    B. If you depart at an airport with a control tower, the ground controller automatically activates your flight plan after you take off.
    C. Filing and opening a flight plan ensures that Search and Rescue (SAR) organizations can locate you if you do not reach your destination and close your flight plan.

STAGE III

31. If you have several cruising altitudes selected for a flight, what altitude should be entered in the Altitude field of the flight plan?
    A. List only the last cruising altitude.
    B. List only the initial cruising altitude.
    C. Enter all planned altitudes along your route of flight.

32. If you activate a flight plan at 1930Z and your time enroute to the destination is 2 hours and 40 minutes, at what time will ATC begin a telephone search if you have not closed the flight plan?
    A. 2200Z
    B. 2210Z
    C. 2240Z

VOR NAVIGATION

Refer to the following chart excerpt to answer questions 33, 34, and 35.

33. The VOR is tuned to Dodge City VORTAC, and the airplane is positioned over Ensign, a small town southwest of the VORTAC (see arrow). Which VOR indication is correct?
    A. 1
    B. 2
    C. 3

34. The VOR is tuned to the Garden City VORTAC. The omnibearing selector (OBS) is set on 090°, with a FROM indication and a right course deviation indicator (CDI) deflection. What is the airplane's position from the VORTAC?
    A. Southeast
    B. Northeast
    C. Northwest

35. What is the approximate position of your airplane if the VOR receivers indicate the 095° radial of Garden City VORTAC and the 255° radial of Dodge City VORTAC?
    A. Jetmore Airport (K79)
    B. Cimarron Airport (8K8)
    C. Montezuma Airport (K17)

36. What should the omnibearing selector (OBS) and TO-FROM indicator read when the course deviation indicator (CDI) needle is centered using a VOR test signal (VOT)?
    A. 180° FROM only if the airplane is due north of the VOT
    B. 0° TO or 180° FROM, regardless of the airplane's position from the VOT
    C. 0° FROM or 180° TO, regardless of the airplane's position from the VOT

SATELLITE NAVIGATION – GPS

37. Which is an action that you should take when navigating with GPS?
    A. Enter the latitude and longitude of all the waypoints you are using for the flight.
    B. Prior to flight, verify that the navigation database and other databases are current.
    C. Activate the course to the next waypoint each time the airplane passes over a waypoint in your flight plan.

38. Select the true statement regarding RAIM.
    A. RAIM is a method by which the GPS receiver computes the aircraft position, track, and groundspeed.
    B. RAIM uses a series of ground stations that generate a corrective message to improve navigational accuracy.
    C. Methods to verify that RAIM will be available include checking NOTAMs and using your GPS receiver's RAIM monitoring and prediction functions.

39. What is a method that you can use to navigate with GPS?
    A. Use Direct-To navigation to create a route using several waypoints.
    B. Use Direct-To navigation to fly from your present position directly to a waypoint.
    C. Select the flight plan feature to have the GPS equipment automatically create a route to your destination using waypoints in the database.

40. You are near an airport waypoint, using the GPS for VFR navigation. Which is true about the navigation indicator shown?
    A. The CDI sensitivity is in the approach mode.
    B. The CDI displays the angular deviation from the course.
    C. The distance from your present position to the desired track is 1.0 nautical mile.

41. Which is an indication of waypoint passage that GPS equipment might display?
    A. The GPS automatically switches to CDI mode.
    B. The moving map shows the active leg in green.
    C. Navigation information for the next leg is displayed.

42. Select the true statement regarding using a GPS moving map display.
    A. The active leg of your flight is typically green on the moving map.
    B. Failing to use the moving map as the primary navigation source is a common error.
    C. The moving map display provides supplemental navigation data and is not required to meet the certification standards of the primary navigation CDI.

Applying Human Factors Principles

AVIATION PHYSIOLOGY

43. What part of your eye allows you to perceive color?
    A. Lens
    B. Rods
    C. Cones

44. What action should you take to enable your eyes to adapt to darkness for a night flight?
    A. Use low-level blue-white light for two hours prior to the flight.
    B. Wear dark glasses that block all wavelengths of light except blue for one hour before the flight.
    C. Avoid bright white lights, such as headlights, landing lights, strobe lights and flashlights for at least 30 minutes before flight.

45. What is the best way to view dim objects at night?
    A. Scan around the object, then stare at it.
    B. Stare directly at the object for a few moments, then scan around it.
    C. Use off-center viewing and avoid staring at the object for too long.

46. What situations can increase the risk of flying a lower-than-normal approach?
    A. A wide runway
    B. A runway that slopes downhill
    C. Flying over water, at night, or over featureless terrain

47. Select the true statement regarding maintaining orientation in flight.
    A. If you experience spatial disorientation during flight in restricted visibility, rely on the aircraft instrument indications.
    B. You are more susceptible to spatial disorientation if you use the instruments to interpret flight attitude rather than body signals.
    C. During a prolonged, constant-rate turn, you typically sense an increased turning motion because the fluid in your semicircular canals reaches equilibrium.

48. What is the best way to overcome the effects of hypoxia?
    A. Climb to a higher altitude.
    B. Use supplemental oxygen.
    C. Breathe slowly into a paper bag.

STAGE III

49. Which is a cause of hyperventilation?
    A. Stress
    B. Lack of oxygen
    C. Lack of proper nourishment

SINGLE-PILOT RESOURCE MANAGEMENT

50. Select the true statement regarding single-pilot resource management concepts.
    A. You are maintaining situational awareness if you know the airplane's position on your route of flight at all times.
    B. You are required to follow the standard operating procedures (SOPs) in your airplane's POH to ensure all checklist items are completed.
    C. An automation surprise occurs when an automation system does something you do not expect, or fails to do something you do expect.

51. The visibility is decreasing and the cloud ceiling appears to be lowering ahead on your route of flight. You think to yourself: *"I can do this. I'll just descend below the clouds and even if I enter IFR conditions, I'm excellent at attitude instrument flying."* What type of hazardous attitude are you exhibiting and what is the appropriate antidote?
    A. Macho; antidote—*taking chances is foolish.*
    B. Resignation; antidote—*I'm not helpless. I can make a difference.*
    C. Anti-authority; antidote—*follow the rules. They are usually right.*

52. The "I'M SAFE" checklist helps you accomplish what action?
    A. Assess your fitness for flight
    B. Recall the before-landing briefing items
    C. Verify you have checked each item during the preflight inspection

53. Select the true statement regarding the aeronautical decision making (ADM) process.
    A. The ADM process is primarily used during emergency situations only.
    B. The ADM process typically ends when you choose a course of action after considering your options.
    C. Evaluating the outcome of your decision to determine if additional steps need to be taken is part of the ADM process.

54. It is early spring and the past two weekends have been stormy with poor visibility. After work on Friday you plan to fly your family to a popular national park, where you have reserved a cabin a year in advance. Although you are current to fly at night, you have very little night flying experience and part of the flight will occur after dark. No squawks are reported for the airplane, but the annual inspection is due the day after your scheduled return. Select the true statement about using the 5Ps to assess risk for this flight.
    A. Using the 5Ps to assess risk in flight is not necessary if you mitigate all risks during flight planning.
    B. A risk associated with the Pilot is the your fitness for flight—you could be tired at the end of your work week and you lack extensive night flying experience.
    C. The annual inspection is not a Plane risk factor because you can fly with an expired annual back to the departure airport for the inspection if weather delays the return flight.

55. You receive a landing clearance and are on short final when your friend, who is a pilot offers a critique about your traffic pattern entry. Which statement is true regarding the sterile cockpit procedure?
    A. Even if your friend's comments are distracting, you should make time for these conversations because they might contain essential flight safety information.
    B. The sterile cockpit rule prohibits private pilots from performing non-essential duties or activities during taxi, takeoff, landing, and other noncruise flight operations.
    C. Private pilots are strongly recommended to follow a sterile cockpit procedure to increase safety, asking passengers to defer questions or conversations during high-workload times.

STAGE III

Flying Cross-Country

THE FLIGHT PLANNING PROCESS

Use the sectional chart excerpt as needed to answer questions 56 and 57.

STAGE III

56. It is Friday, and you are planning a flight from Hudson Valley Regional (KPOU) in New York to Bradley International Airport (KBDL) in Connecticut the coming weekend. What is an action that you should you take to formulate a flight overview?
    A. Check the current weather by obtaining a standard weather briefing, then complete the nav log.
    B. Review an aeronautical chart for any special use airspace along the route to determine if the flight is practicable.
    C. Begin by selecting easily identifiable checkpoints along the route, such as prominent landmarks and navaids, to keep track of your position.

57. What factors apply to determining route data as you develop a route from Hudson Valley Regional (KPOU) to Bradley International Airport (KBDL)?
    A. Because the route distance is 57 nautical miles and you typically cruise at about 90 knots, your approximate time enroute is 58 minutes.
    B. A cruising altitude of 6,500 feet MSL would allow you to meet VFR cruising altitude requirements and clear any obstacles along the route.
    C. Barkhamsted Reservoir about 12 nautical miles from Bradley airport just north of a direct course would make a good visual checkpoint for contacting Bradley approach.

THE FLIGHT

58. What is an example of an action that you perform during the enroute phase of flight?
    A. Visualize your entry into the traffic pattern and perform the before-landing briefing.
    B. Request a clearance from ATC to transition through airspace designated as restricted.
    C. If your flight time is significantly longer than you originally planned, you might need to revise your flight plan, including adding a fuel stop, if necessary.

59. What postflight actions should you take?
    A. Verify that ground control has closed your flight plan.
    B. Taxi to parking, close your flight plan, and evaluate the flight.
    C. Perform a postflight inspection and delete your GPS flight plan.

STAGE III

STAGE III

Private Pilot
End of Course Exam A

The end-of-course exams are the final preparation for the Private Pilot Airman Knowledge Exam. To make your preparation for the FAA airmen knowledge test as effective as possible, this exam contains similar questions and figures to those used in the actual tests. If you are training under Part 141, you must take both Exam A and Exam B. Your instructor will grade each exam and assign weak subject areas for review.

If you are training under Part 61, complete one of the exams as assigned by your instructor. The instructor will assign the other exam if you need additional practice. After a thorough review, you should schedule and take the FAA Private Pilot Airman Knowledge Test right away.

Completely darken only one circle for each question on the answer form.

1. If the grade of fuel used in an aircraft engine is lower than specified for the engine, it will most likely cause
    A. a mixture of fuel and air that is not uniform in all cylinders.
    B. lower cylinder head temperatures.
    C. detonation.

2. What type fuel can be substituted for an aircraft if the recommended octane is not available?
    A. The next higher octane aviation gas.
    B. The next lower octane aviation gas.
    C. Unleaded automotive gas of the same octane rating.

3. Which instrument will become inoperative if the pitot tube becomes clogged?
    A. Altimeter.
    B. Vertical speed.
    C. Airspeed.

4. What is density altitude?
    A. The height above the standard datum plane.
    B. The pressure altitude corrected for nonstandard temperature.
    C. The altitude read directly from the altimeter.

5. What is the maximum flaps-extended speed?
    A. 58 knots.
    B. 100 knots.
    C. 165 knots.

6. Deviation in a magnetic compass is caused by the
   A. presence of flaws in the permanent magnets of the compass.
   B. difference in the location between true north and magnetic north.
   C. magnetic fields within the aircraft distorting the lines of magnetic force.

7. If a flight is made from an area of high pressure into an area of lower pressure without the altimeter setting being adjusted, the altimeter will indicate
   A. lower than the actual altitude above sea level.
   B. higher than the actual altitude above sea level.
   C. the actual altitude above sea level.

8. The four forces acting on an airplane in flight are
   A. lift, weight, thrust, and drag.
   B. lift, weight, gravity, and thrust.
   C. lift, gravity, power, and friction.

9. An airplane said to be inherently stable will
   A. be difficult to stall.
   B. require less effort to control.
   C. not spin.

10. The left turning tendency of an airplane caused by P-factor is the result of the
    A. clockwise rotation of the engine and the propeller turning the airplane counter-clockwise.
    B. propeller blade descending on the right, producing more thrust than the ascending blade on the left.
    C. gyroscopic forces applied to the rotating propeller blades acting 90° in advance of the point the force was applied.

11. If an airplane weighs 2,300 pounds, what approximate weight would the airplane structure be required to support during a 60° banked turn while maintaining altitude?
    A. 2,300 pounds.
    B. 3,400 pounds.
    C. 4,600 pounds.

ANGLE OF BANK ϕ	LOAD FACTOR n
0°	1.0
10°	1.015
30°	1.154
45°	1.414
60°	2.000
70°	2.923
80°	5.747
85°	11.473
90°	∞

LOAD FACTOR CHART

LOAD FACTOR – G UNITS

BANK ANGLE – IN DEGREES

12. Prior to starting each maneuver, pilots should
    A. check altitude, airspeed, and heading indications.
    B. visually scan the entire area for collision avoidance.
    C. announce their intentions on the nearest CTAF.

13. Illustration A indicates that the aircraft is
    A. below the glide slope.
    B. on the glide slope.
    C. above the glide slope.

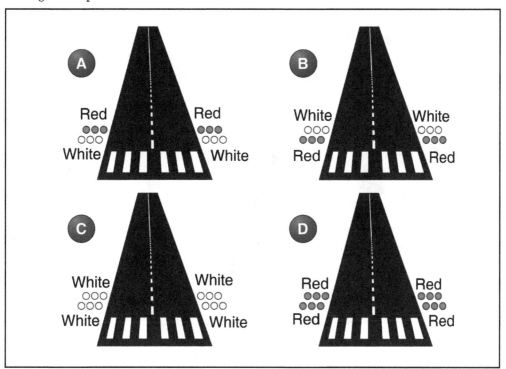

14. Area C on the airport depicted is classified as a
    A. stabilized area.
    B. multiple heliport.
    C. closed runway.

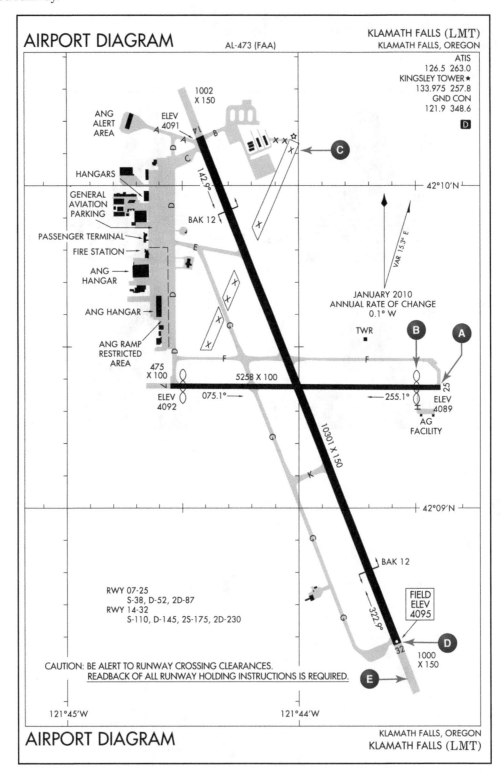

AIRPORT DIAGRAM

AL-473 (FAA)

KLAMATH FALLS (LMT)
KLAMATH FALLS, OREGON

ATIS
126.5 263.0
KINGSLEY TOWER ★
133.975 257.8
GND CON
121.9 348.6

ANG
ALERT
AREA

ELEV
4091

1002
X 150

142.9°

BAK 12

HANGARS

GENERAL
AVIATION
PARKING

PASSENGER TERMINAL

FIRE STATION

ANG
HANGAR

ANG HANGAR

ANG RAMP
RESTRICTED
AREA

475
X 100

ELEV
4092

5258 X 100

075.1°

255.1°

ELEV
4089

AG
FACILITY

VAR 15.3° E

JANUARY 2010
ANNUAL RATE OF CHANGE
0.1° W

TWR

42°10'N

10301 X 150

322.9°

BAK 12

FIELD
ELEV
4095

1000
X 150

42°09'N

RWY 07-25
S-38, D-52, 2D-87
RWY 14-32
S-110, D-145, 2S-175, 2D-230

CAUTION: BE ALERT TO RUNWAY CROSSING CLEARANCES.
READBACK OF ALL RUNWAY HOLDING INSTRUCTIONS IS REQUIRED.

121°45'W

121°44'W

AIRPORT DIAGRAM

KLAMATH FALLS, OREGON
KLAMATH FALLS (LMT)

48

Use the following figure to answer questions 15 and 16.

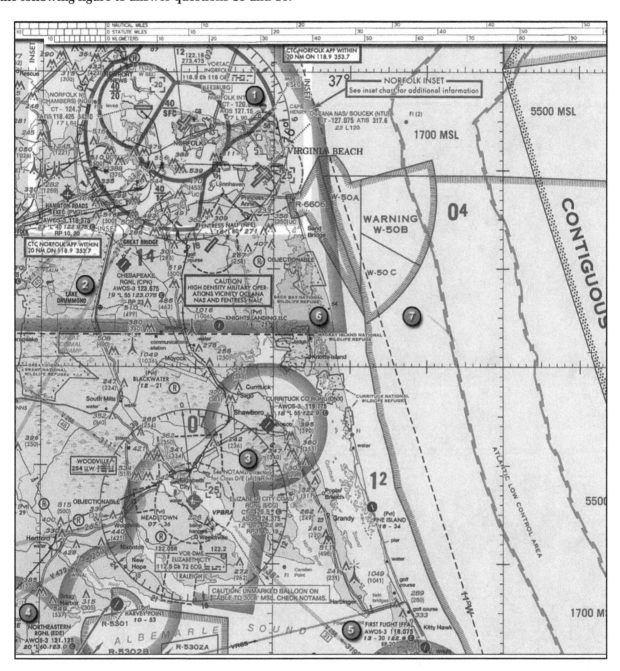

15. (Area 3) Determine the approximate latitude and longitude of Currituck County Airport.
    A. 36°24'N - 76°01'W.
    B. 36°48'N - 76°01'W.
    C. 47°24'N - 75°58'W.

16. (Area 2) The flag symbol at Lake Drummond represents a
    A. compulsory reporting point for the Norfolk Class C Airspace.
    B. compulsory reporting point for Hampton Roads Airport.
    C. visual checkpoint used to identify position for initial callup to Norfolk Approach Control.

END OF COURSE EXAM A

17. (Area 1) What minimum altitude is necessary to vertically clear the obstacle on the northeast side of Airpark East Airport by 500 feet?
    A. 1,010 feet MSL.
    B. 1,273 feet MSL.
    C. 1,283 feet MSL.

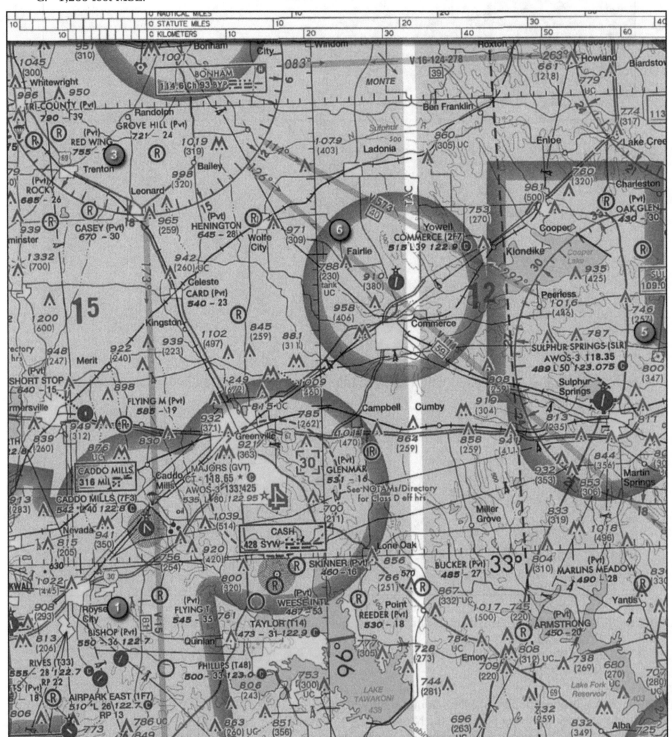

18. An operable 4096-code transponder and Mode C encoding altimeter are required in
    A. Class B airspace and within 30 miles of the Class B primary airport.
    B. Class D airspace.
    C. Class E airspace below 10,000 feet MSL.

19. (Area 3) What is the floor of the Savannah Class C airspace at the shelf area (outer circle)?
  A. 1,300 feet AGL
  B. 1,300 feet MSL
  C. 1,700 feet MSL

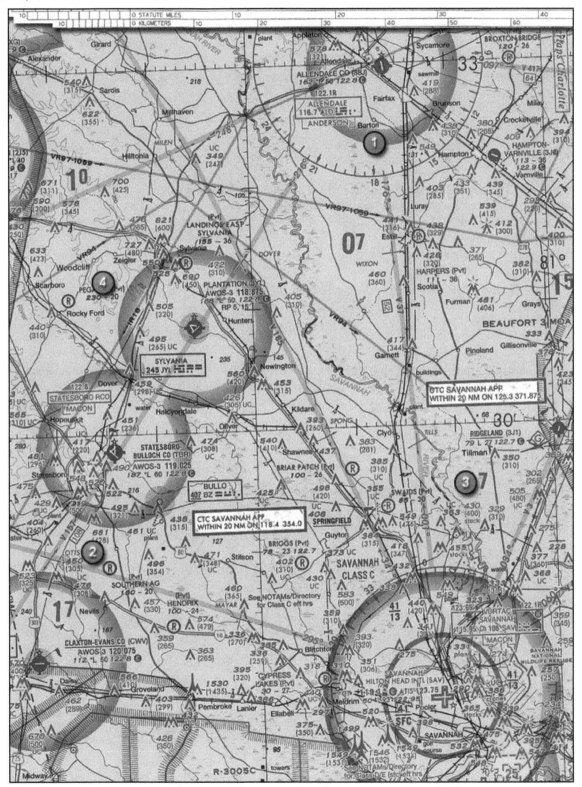

20. The upper limit of Class C airspace above the primary airport is normally
    A. 1,200 feet AGL.
    B. 3,000 feet AGL.
    C. 4,000 feet AGL.

21. The normal radius of the outer area of Class C airspace is
    A. 5 nautical miles.
    B. 15 nautical miles.
    C. 20 nautical miles.

22. Responsibility for collision avoidance in an alert area rests with
    A. the controlling agency.
    B. all pilots.
    C. air traffic control.

23. A non-tower satellite airport, within the same Class D airspace as that designated for the primary airport, requires radio communications be established and maintained with the
    A. satellite airport's UNICOM.
    B. associated Flight Service facility.
    C. primary airport's control tower.

24. What ATC facility should the pilot contact to receive a special VFR departure clearance in Class D airspace?
    A. Flight Service
    B. Air traffic control tower.
    C. Air route traffic control center.

25. An aircraft departs an airport in the eastern daylight time zone at 0945 EDT for a 2-hour flight to an airport located in the central daylight time zone. The landing should be at what coordinated universal time?
    A. 1345Z.
    B. 1445Z.
    C. 1545Z.

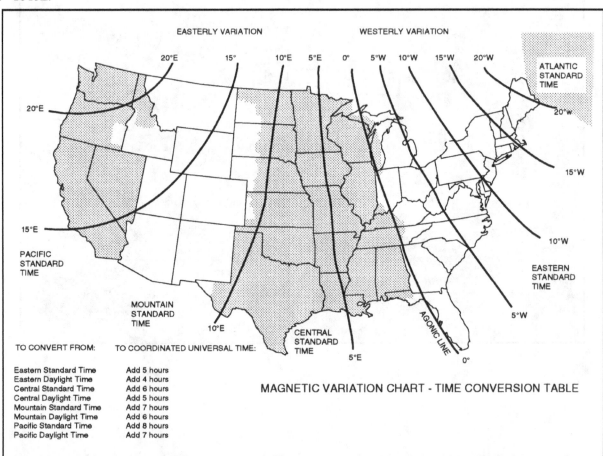

MAGNETIC VARIATION CHART - TIME CONVERSION TABLE

TO CONVERT FROM:	TO COORDINATED UNIVERSAL TIME:
Eastern Standard Time	Add 5 hours
Eastern Daylight Time	Add 4 hours
Central Standard Time	Add 6 hours
Central Daylight Time	Add 5 hours
Mountain Standard Time	Add 7 hours
Mountain Daylight Time	Add 6 hours
Pacific Standard Time	Add 8 hours
Pacific Daylight Time	Add 7 hours

26. (Area 3) What is the recommended communications procedure for a landing at Currituck County Airport?
   A. Transmit intentions on 122.9 MHz when 10 miles out and give position reports in the traffic pattern.
   B. Contact Elizabeth City FSS for airport advisory service
   C. Contact new Bern FSS for area traffic information.

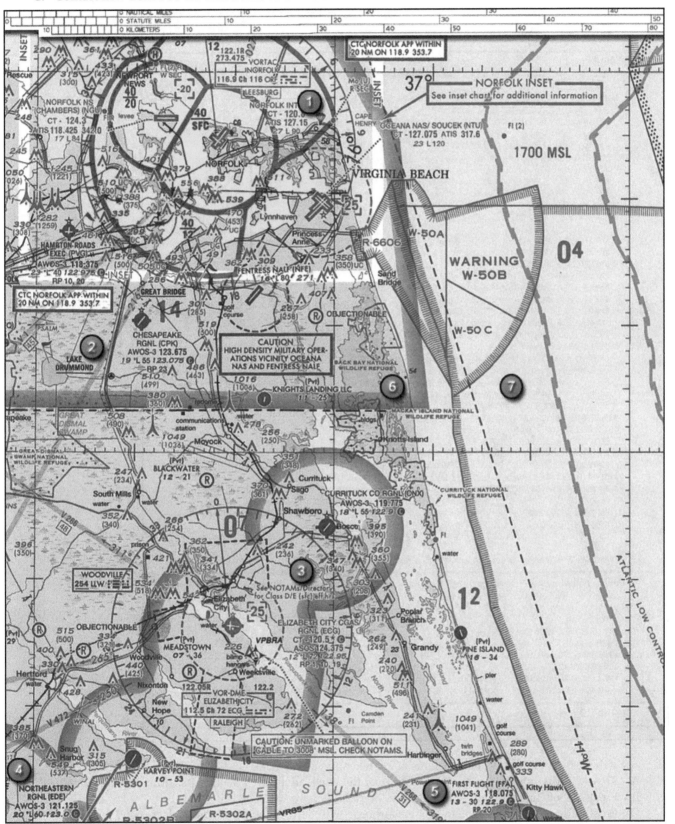

END OF COURSE EXAM A

27. Where is Loup City Municipal located with relation to the city?
    A. Northeast approximately 3 miles
    B. Northwest approximately 1 mile
    C. East approximately 10 miles

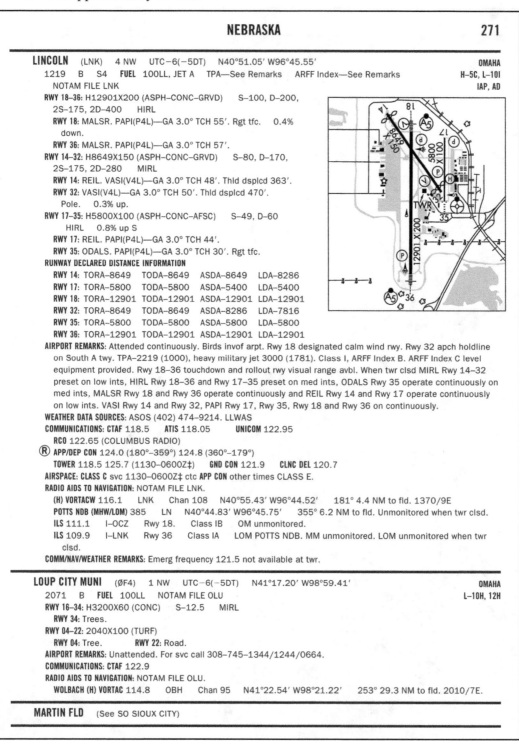

NEBRASKA 271

LINCOLN (LNK) 4 NW UTC−6(−5DT) N40°51.05′ W96°45.55′   OMAHA
  1219 B S4 **FUEL** 100LL, JET A TPA—See Remarks ARFF Index—See Remarks   H−5C, L−10I
  NOTAM FILE LNK   IAP, AD
  RWY 18−36: H12901X200 (ASPH−CONC−GRVD) S−100, D−200,
    2S−175, 2D−400 HIRL
    RWY 18: MALSR. PAPI(P4L)—GA 3.0° TCH 55′. Rgt tfc. 0.4%
    down.
    RWY 36: MALSR. PAPI(P4L)—GA 3.0° TCH 57′.
  RWY 14−32: H8649X150 (ASPH−CONC−GRVD) S−80, D−170,
    2S−175, 2D−280 MIRL
    RWY 14: REIL. VASI(V4L)—GA 3.0° TCH 48′. Thld dsplcd 363′.
    RWY 32: VASI(V4L)—GA 3.0° TCH 50′. Thld dsplcd 470′.
    Pole. 0.3% up.
  RWY 17−35: H5800X100 (ASPH−CONC−AFSC) S−49, D−60
    HIRL 0.8% up S
    RWY 17: REIL. PAPI(P4L)—GA 3.0° TCH 44′.
    RWY 35: ODALS. PAPI(P4L)—GA 3.0° TCH 30′. Rgt tfc.
  RUNWAY DECLARED DISTANCE INFORMATION
    RWY 14: TORA−8649 TODA−8649 ASDA−8649 LDA−8286
    RWY 17: TORA−5800 TODA−5800 ASDA−5400 LDA−5400
    RWY 18: TORA−12901 TODA−12901 ASDA−12901 LDA−12901
    RWY 32: TORA−8649 TODA−8649 ASDA−8286 LDA−7816
    RWY 35: TORA−5800 TODA−5800 ASDA−5800 LDA−5800
    RWY 36: TORA−12901 TODA−12901 ASDA−12901 LDA−12901
  AIRPORT REMARKS: Attended continuously. Birds invof arpt. Rwy 18 designated calm wind rwy. Rwy 32 apch holdline
    on South A twy. TPA−2219 (1000), heavy military jet 3000 (1781). Class I, ARFF Index B. ARFF Index C level
    equipment provided. Rwy 18−36 touchdown and rollout rwy visual range avbl. When twr clsd MIRL Rwy 14−32
    preset on low ints, HIRL Rwy 18−36 and Rwy 17−35 preset on med ints, ODALS Rwy 35 operate continuously on
    med ints, MALSR Rwy 18 and Rwy 36 operate continuously and REIL Rwy 14 and Rwy 17 operate continuously
    on low ints. VASI Rwy 14 and Rwy 32, PAPI Rwy 17, Rwy 35, Rwy 18 and Rwy 36 on continuously.
  WEATHER DATA SOURCES: ASOS (402) 474−9214. LLWAS
  COMMUNICATIONS: CTAF 118.5 **ATIS** 118.05 **UNICOM** 122.95
    RCO 122.65 (COLUMBUS RADIO)
  ®️ **APP/DEP CON** 124.0 (180°−359°) 124.8 (360°−179°)
    TOWER 118.5 125.7 (1130−0600Z‡) **GND CON** 121.9 **CLNC DEL** 120.7
  AIRSPACE: CLASS C svc 1130−0600Z‡ ctc **APP CON** other times CLASS E.
  RADIO AIDS TO NAVIGATION: NOTAM FILE LNK.
    (H) VORTACW 116.1 LNK Chan 108 N40°55.43′ W96°44.52′ 181° 4.4 NM to fld. 1370/9E
    POTTS NDB (MHW/LOM) 385 LN N40°44.83′ W96°45.75′ 355° 6.2 NM to fld. Unmonitored when twr clsd.
    ILS 111.1 I−OCZ Rwy 18. Class IB OM unmonitored.
    ILS 109.9 I−LNK Rwy 36 Class IA LOM POTTS NDB. MM unmonitored. LOM unmonitored when twr
    clsd.
  COMM/NAV/WEATHER REMARKS: Emerg frequency 121.5 not available at twr.

LOUP CITY MUNI (ØF4) 1 NW UTC−6(−5DT) N41°17.20′ W98°59.41′   OMAHA
  2071 B **FUEL** 100LL NOTAM FILE OLU   L−10H, 12H
  RWY 16−34: H3200X60 (CONC) S−12.5 MIRL
    RWY 34: Trees.
  RWY 04−22: 2040X100 (TURF)
    RWY 04: Tree. **RWY 22:** Road.
  AIRPORT REMARKS: Unattended. For svc call 308−745−1344/1244/0664.
  COMMUNICATIONS: CTAF 122.9
  RADIO AIDS TO NAVIGATION: NOTAM FILE OLU.
    WOLBACH (H) VORTAC 114.8 OBH Chan 95 N41°22.54′ W98°21.22′ 253° 29.3 NM to fld. 2010/7E.

MARTIN FLD (See SO SIOUX CITY)

28. How will frost on the wings of an airplane affect takeoff performance?
    A. Frost will disrupt the smooth flow of air over the wing, adversely affecting its lifting capability.
    B. Frost will change the camber of the wing, increasing its lifting capability.
    C. Frost will cause the airplane to become airborne with a higher angle of attack, decreasing the stall speed.

29. A temperature inversion would most likely result in which weather condition?
    A. Clouds with extensive vertical development above an inversion aloft.
    B. Good visibility in the lower levels of the atmosphere and poor visibility above an inversion aloft.
    C. An increase in temperature as altitude is increased.

30. Steady precipitation preceding a front is an indication of
    A. stratiform clouds with moderate turbulence.
    B. cumuliform clouds with little or no turbulence.
    C. stratiform clouds with little or no turbulence.

31. Crests of standing mountain waves may be marked by stationary, lens-shaped clouds known as
    A. mammatocumulus clouds.
    B. standing lenticular clouds.
    C. roll clouds.

32. Why is frost considered hazardous to flight?
    A. Frost changes the basic aerodynamic shape of the airfoils, thereby decreasing lift.
    B. Frost slows the airflow over the airfoils, thereby increasing control effectiveness.
    C. Frost spoils the smooth flow of air over the wings, thereby decreasing lifting capability.

33. The greatest vortex strength occurs when the generating aircraft is
    A. light, dirty, and fast.
    B. heavy, dirty, and fast.
    C. heavy, clean, and slow.

Use the following figure to answer questions 34 and 35.

TAF	
KMEM	121720Z 121818 20012KT 5SM HZ BKN030 PROB40 2022 1SM TSRA OVC008CB
	FM2200 33015G20KT P6SM BKN015 OVC025 PROB40 2202 3SM SHRA
	FM0200 35012KT OVC008 PROB40 0205 2SM-RASN BECMG 0608 02008KT BKN012
	BECMG 1012 00000KT 3SM BR SKC TEMPO 1214 1/2SM FG
	FM1600 VRB06KT P6SM SKC=
KOKC	051130Z 051212 14008KT 5SM BR BKN030 TEMPO 1316 1 1/2SM BR
	FM1600 18010KT P6SM SKC BECMG 2224 20013G20KT 4SM SHRA OVC020
	PROB40 0006 2SM TSRA OVC008CB BECMG 0608 21015KT P6SM SCT040=

34. What is the valid period for the TAF for KMEM?
    A. 1200Z to 1200Z.
    B. 1200Z to 1800Z.
    C. 1800Z to 1800Z.

35. Between 1000Z and 1200Z the visibility at KMEM is forecast to be?
    A. 1/2 statute mile.
    B. 3 statute miles.
    C. 6 statute miles.

36. What is indicated when a current CONVECTIVE SIGMET forecasts thunderstorms?
    A. Moderate thunderstorms covering 30 percent of the area.
    B. Moderate or severe turbulence.
    C. Thunderstorms obscured by massive cloud layers.

37. How are low-level significant weather (sigwx) prognostic charts best used by a pilot?
    A. For overall planning at all altitudes.
    B. For determining areas to avoid (freezing levels and turbulence).
    C. For analyzing current frontal activity and cloud coverage.

38. What effect, if any, does high humidity have on aircraft performance?
    A. It increases performance.
    B. It decreases performance.
    C. It has no effect on performance.

39. Determine the total distance required to land over a 50-foot obstacle.

    Pressure altitude.............................3,750 feet

    Headwind ....12 knots

    Temperature.................................... standard
    A. 794 feet
    B. 836 feet
    C. 816 feet

		AT SEA LEVEL & 59 °F		AT 2500 FT & 50 °F		AT 5000 FT & 41 °F		AT 7500 FT & 32 °F	
GROSS WEIGHT LB	APPROACH SPEED, IAS, MPH	GROUND ROLL	TOTAL TO CLEAR 50 FT OBS	GROUND ROLL	TOTAL TO CLEAR 50 FT OBS	GROUND ROLL	TOTAL TO CLEAR 50 FT OBS	GROUND ROLL	TOTAL TO CLEAR 50 FT OBS
1600	60	445	1075	470	1135	495	1195	520	1255

LANDING DISTANCE — FLAPS LOWERED TO 40 ° - POWER OFF
HARD SURFACE RUNWAY - ZERO WIND

NOTES: 1. Decrease the distances shown by 10% for each 4 knots of headwind.
2. Increase the distance by 10% for each 60 °F temperature increase above standard.
3. For operation on a dry, grass runway, increase distances (both "ground roll" and "total to clear 50 ft obstacle") by 20% of the "total to clear 50 ft obstacle" figure.

40. Determine if the airplane weight and balance is within limits.

  Front seat occupants .... 415 pounds
  Rear seat occupants .... 110 pounds
  Fuel, main tanks .... 44 gallons
  Fuel, aux tanks .... 19 gallons
  Baggage .... 32 pounds

 A. 19 pounds overweight, CG within limits
 B. 19 pounds overweight, CG out of limits forward
 C. Weight within limits, CG out of limits

Useful load weights and moments

Baggage or 5th seat occupant — ARM 140

Weight	Moment/100
10	14
20	28
30	42
40	56
50	70
60	84
70	98
80	112
90	126
100	140
110	154
120	168
130	182
140	196
150	210
160	224
170	238
180	252
190	266
200	280
210	294
220	308
230	322
240	336
250	350
260	364
270	378

Occupants

Front seats ARM 85		Rear seats ARM 121	
Weight	Moment/100	Weight	Moment/100
120	102	120	145
130	110	130	157
140	119	140	169
150	128	150	182
160	136	160	194
170	144	170	206
180	153	180	218
190	162	190	230
200	170	200	242

Usable fuel

Main wing tanks ARM 75

Gallons	Weight	Moment/100
5	30	22
10	60	45
15	90	68
20	120	90
25	150	112
30	180	135
35	210	158
40	240	180
44	264	198

Auxiliary wing tanks ARM 94

Gallons	Weight	Moment/100
5	30	28
10	60	56
15	90	85
19	114	107

*Oil

Quarts	Weight	Moment/100
10	19	5

*Included in basic empty weight.

Empty weight~2,015
MOM/100~1,554
Moment limits vs weight
Moment limits are based on the following weight and center of gravity limit data (landing gear down).

Weight condition	Forward CG limit	AFT CG limit
2,950 lb (takeoff or landing)	82.1	84.7
2,525 lb	77.5	85.7
2,475 lb or less	77.0	85.7

Moment limits vs weight (continued)

Weight	Minimum Moment/100	Maximum Moment/100	Weight	Minimum Moment/100	Maximum Moment/100
2,100	1,617	1,800	2,500	1,932	2,143
2,110	1,625	1,808	2,510	1,942	2,151
2,120	1,632	1,817	2,520	1,953	2,160
2,130	1,640	1,825	2,530	1,963	2,168
2,140	1,648	1,834	2,540	1,974	2,176
2,150	1,656	1,843	2,550	1,984	2,184
2,160	1,663	1,851	2,560	1,995	2,192
2,170	1,671	1,860	2,570	2,005	2,200
2,180	1,679	1,868	2,580	2,016	2,208
2,190	1,686	1,877	2,590	2,026	2,216
2,200	1,694	1,885	2,600	2,037	2,224
2,210	1,702	1,894	2,610	2,048	2,232
2,220	1,709	1,903	2,620	2,058	2,239
2,230	1,717	1,911	2,630	2,069	2,247
2,240	1,725	1,920	2,640	2,080	2,255
2,250	1,733	1,928	2,650	2,090	2,263
2,260	1,740	1,937	2,660	2,101	2,271
2,270	1,748	1,945	2,670	2,112	2,279
2,280	1,756	1,954	2,680	2,123	2,287
2,290	1,763	1,963	2,690	2,133	2,295
2,300	1,771	1,971	2,700	2,144	2,303
2,310	1,779	1,980	2,710	2,155	2,311
2,320	1,786	1,988	2,720	2,166	2,319
2,330	1,794	1,997	2,730	2,177	2,326
2,340	1,802	2,005	2,740	2,188	2,334
2,350	1,810	2,014	2,750	2,199	2,342
2,360	1,817	2,023	2,760	2,210	2,350
2,370	1,825	2,031	2,770	2,221	2,358
2,380	1,833	2,040	2,780	2,232	2,366
2,390	1,840	2,048	2,790	2,243	2,374
2,400	1,848	2,057	2,800	2,254	2,381
2,410	1,856	2,065	2,810	2,265	2,389
2,420	1,863	2,074	2,820	2,276	2,397
2,430	1,871	2,083	2,830	2,287	2,405
2,440	1,879	2,091	2,840	2,298	2,413
2,450	1,887	2,100	2,850	2,309	2,421
2,460	1,894	2,108	2,860	2,320	2,428
2,470	1,902	2,117	2,870	2,332	2,436
2,480	1,911	2,125	2,880	2,343	2,444
2,490	1,921	2,134	2,890	2,354	2,452
			2,900	2,365	2,460
			2,910	2,377	2,468
			2,920	2,388	2,475
			2,930	2,399	2,483
			2,940	2,411	2,491
			2,950	2,422	2,499

END OF COURSE EXAM A

41. Determine the magnetic heading for a flight from Sandpoint Airport (area 1) to St. Maries Airport (area 4). The wind is from 215° at 25 knots, and the true airspeed is 125 knots.

    A. 172°.

    B. 187°.

    C. 351°.

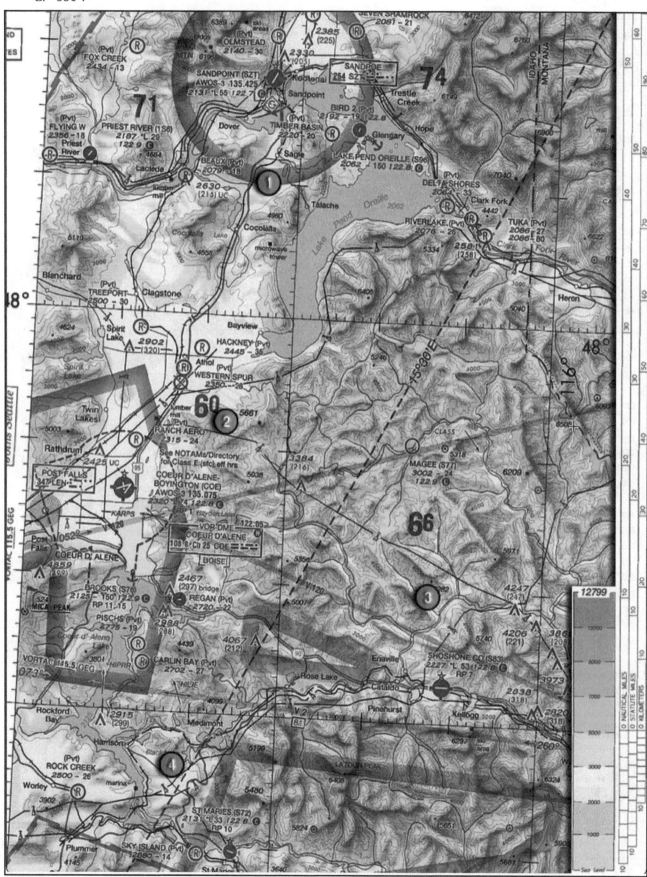

Use the following figure to answer questions 42 and 43.

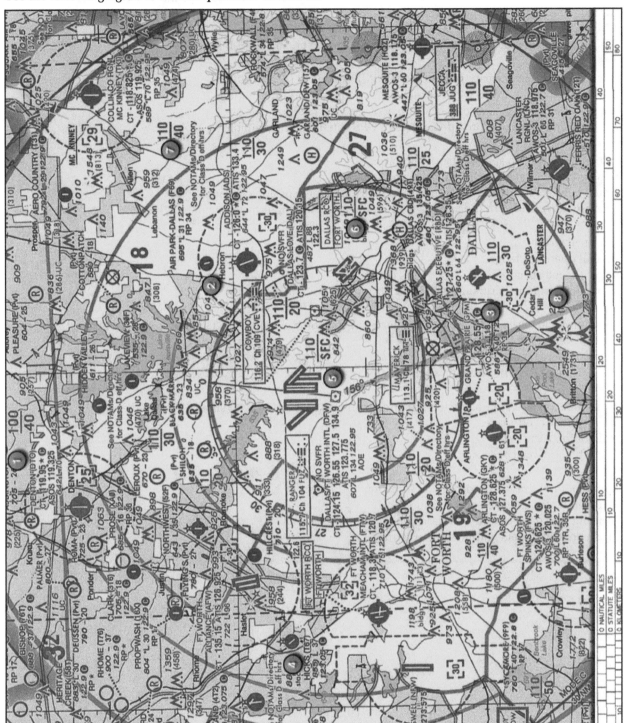

42. (Area 7) The airspace overlying Collin County Mc Kinney Airport (TKI) is controlled from the surface to
   A. 2,900 feet MSL.
   B. 2,500 feet MSL.
   C. 700 feet AGL.

43. (Area 5) The VOR is tuned to the Maverick VOR, which is just south of DFW. The omnibearing selector (OBS) is set on 253°, with a TO indication, and a left course deviation indicator (CDI) deflection. What is the aircraft's position from the VORTAC?
   A. East-northeast.
   B. East-southeast.
   C. West-southwest.

44. The automatic dependent surveillance-broadcast (ADS-B) system includes what primary components?
    A. ADS-B radar transmitter; aircraft radar receiver, ADS-B Out transmitter, and ADS-B In receiver.
    B. ADS-B ground station; aircraft GPS receiver, ADS-B Out transmitter, and ADS-B In receiver.
    C. ADS-B ground station; aircraft VOR/DME or GPS receiver, and ADS-B In receiver.

45. If receiver autonomous integrity monitoring (RAIM) capability is lost in-flight,
    A. the pilot may still rely on GPS derived altitude for vertical information.
    B. the pilot has no assurance of the accuracy of the GPS position.
    C. GPS position is reliable provided at least 3 GPS satellites are available.

46. Pilots are more subject to spatial disorientation if
    A. they ignore the sensations of muscles and inner ear.
    B. visual cues are taken away, as they are in instrument meteorological conditions (IMC).
    C. eyes are moved often in the process of cross-checking the flight instruments.

47. V_{NO} is defined as the
    A. normal operating range.
    B. never-exceed speed.
    C. maximum structural cruising speed.

48. When are non-rechargeable batteries of an emergency locator transmitter (ELT) required to be replaced?
    A. Every 24 months.
    B. When 50 percent of their useful life expires.
    C. At the time of each 100-hour or annual inspection.

49. To determine the expiration date of the last annual aircraft inspection, you should refer to the
    A. airworthiness certificate.
    B. registration certificate.
    C. aircraft maintenance records.

50. Which incident requires an immediate notification to the nearest NTSB field office?
    A. A forced landing due to engine failure.
    B. Landing gear damage, due to a hard landing.
    C. Flight control system malfunction or failure.

END OF COURSE EXAM A

Private Pilot
End of Course Exam B

The end-of-course exams are the final preparation for the Private Pilot Airman Knowledge Exam. To make your preparation for the FAA airmen knowledge test as effective as possible, this exam contains similar questions and figures to those used in the actual tests. If you are training under Part 141, you must take both Exam A and Exam B. Your instructor will grade each exam and assign weak subject areas for review.

If you are training under Part 61, complete one of the exams as assigned by your instructor. The instructor will assign the other exam if you need additional practice. After a thorough review, you should schedule and take the FAA Private Pilot Airman Knowledge Test right away.

Completely darken only one circle for each question on the answer form.

1. One purpose of the dual-ignition system on an aircraft engine is to provide for
   A. improved engine performance.
   B. uniform heat distribution.
   C. balanced cylinder head pressure.

2. While cruising at 9,500 feet MSL, the fuel/air mixture is properly adjusted. What will occur if a descent to 4,500 feet MSL is made without readjusting the mixture?
   A. The fuel/air mixture may become excessively lean.
   B. There will be more fuel in the cylinders than is needed for normal combustion, and the excess fuel will absorb heat and cool the engine.
   C. The excessively rich mixture will create higher cylinder head temperatures and may cause detonation.

3. What change occurs in the fuel/air mixture when carburetor heat is applied?
   A. A decrease in rpm results from the lean mixture.
   B. The fuel/air mixture becomes richer.
   C. The fuel/air mixture becomes leaner.

4. The presence of carburetor ice in an aircraft equipped with a fixed-pitch propeller can be verified by applying carburetor heat and noting
   A. an increase in rpm and then a gradual decrease in rpm.
   B. a decrease in rpm and then a constant rpm indication.
   C. a decrease in rpm and then a gradual increase in rpm.

5. The uncontrolled firing of the fuel/air charge in advance of normal spark ignition is known as
   A. combustion.
   B. pre-ignition.
   C. detonation.

6. Altimeter setting is the value to which the barometric pressure scale of the altimeter is set so the altimeter indicates
   A. calibrated altitude at field elevation.
   B. absolute altitude at field elevation.
   C. true altitude at field elevation.

7. Under what condition is indicated altitude the same as true altitude?
   A. If the altimeter has no mechanical error.
   B. When at sea level under standard conditions.
   C. When at 18,000 feet MSL with the altimeter set at 29.92.

END OF COURSE EXAM B

8. As altitude increases, the indicated airspeed at which a given airplane stalls in a particular configuration will
    A. decrease as the true airspeed decreases.
    B. decrease as the true airspeed increases.
    C. remain the same regardless of altitude.

9. Which marking identifies the never-exceed speed?
    A. 100 knots
    B. 165 knots
    C. 208 knots

10. In the Northern Hemisphere, a magnetic compass will normally indicate initially a turn toward the west if
    A. a left turn is entered from a north heading.
    B. a right turn is entered from a north heading.
    C. an aircraft is accelerated while on a north heading.

11. During flight, when are the indications of a magnetic compass accurate?
    A. Only in straight-and-level unaccelerated flight.
    B. As long as the airspeed is constant.
    C. During turns if the bank does not exceed 18°.

12. Under which condition will pressure altitude be equal to true altitude?
    A. When the atmospheric pressure is 29.92 inches Hg.
    B. When standard atmospheric conditions exist.
    C. When indicated altitude is equal to the pressure altitude.

13. What determines the longitudinal stability of an airplane?
    A. The location of the CG with respect to the center of lift.
    B. The effectiveness of the horizontal stabilizer, rudder, and rudder trim tab.
    C. The relationship of thrust and lift to weight and drag.

14. Which aileron positions should a pilot generally use when taxiing in strong quartering headwinds?
    A. Aileron up on the side from which the wind is blowing.
    B. Aileron down on the side from which the wind is blowing.
    C. Ailerons neutral.

15. (Area A) How should the flight controls be held while taxiing a tricycle-gear equipped airplane into a left quartering headwind?
    A. Left aileron up, elevator neutral.
    B. Left aileron down, elevator neutral.
    C. Left aileron up, elevator down.

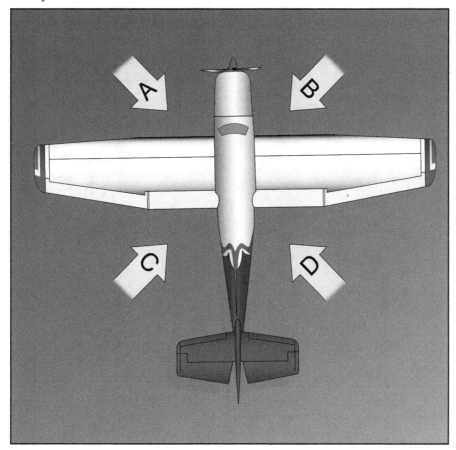

16. Which approach and landing objective is assured when the pilot remains on the proper glidepath of the VASI?
    A. Runway identification and course guidance.
    B. Safe obstruction clearance in the approach area.
    C. Lateral course guidance to the runway.

17. (Area 3) Determine the approximate latitude and longitude of Currituck County Airport.
    A. 36°24'N - 76°01W.
    B. 36°48'N - 76°01W.
    C. 47°24'N - 75°01W.

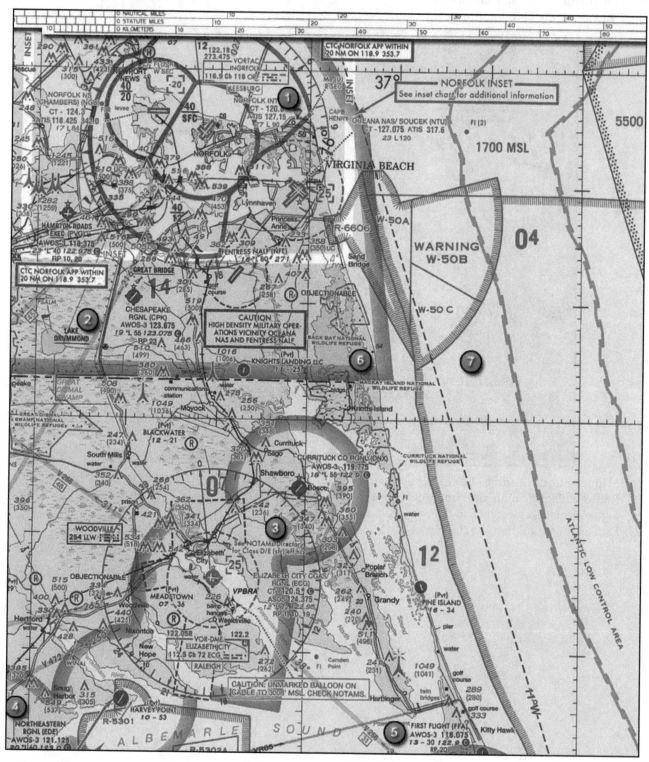

Use the sectional chart and Chart Supplement excerpts to answer Question 18.

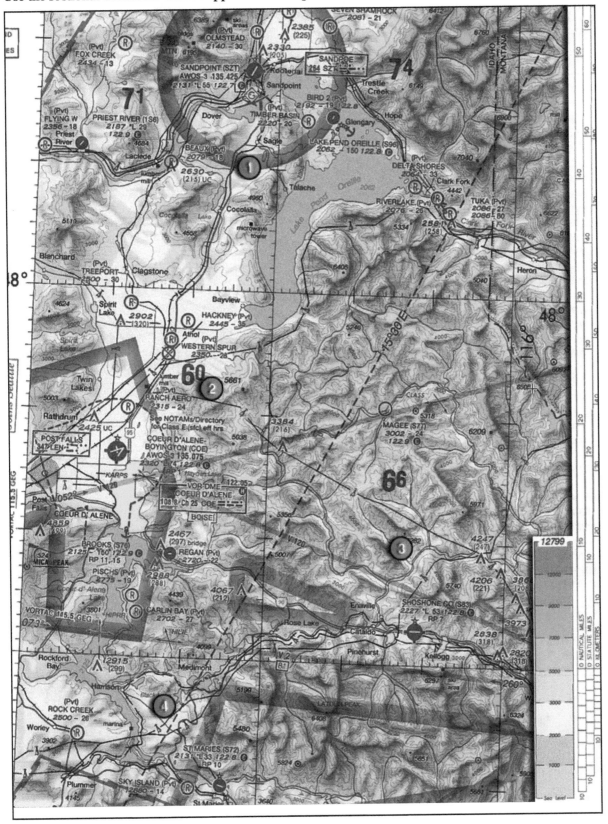

18. (Area 2) At Coeur D'Alene, which frequency should be used as a Common Traffic Advisory Frequency (CTAF) to self-announce position and intentions?
    A. 122.05 MHz.
    B. 122.1/108.8 MHz.
    C. 122.8 MHz.

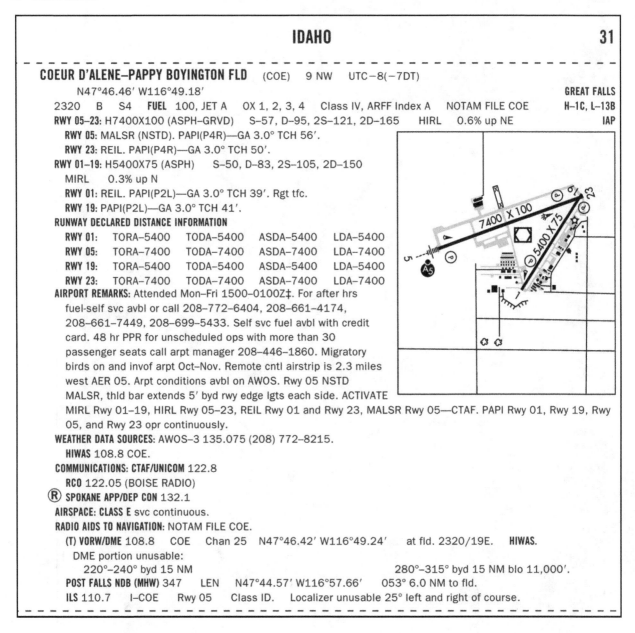

IDAHO   31

COEUR D'ALENE—PAPPY BOYINGTON FLD   (COE)   9 NW   UTC−8(−7DT)
    N47°46.46' W116°49.18'   **GREAT FALLS**
2320   B   S4   **FUEL** 100, JET A   OX 1, 2, 3, 4   Class IV, ARFF Index A   NOTAM FILE COE   **H−1C, L−13B**
RWY 05–23: H7400X100 (ASPH–GRVD)   S−57, D−95, 2S−121, 2D−165   HIRL   0.6% up NE   **IAP**
  RWY 05: MALSR (NSTD). PAPI(P4R)—GA 3.0° TCH 56'.
  RWY 23: REIL. PAPI(P4R)—GA 3.0° TCH 50'.
RWY 01–19: H5400X75 (ASPH)   S−50, D−83, 2S−105, 2D−150
  MIRL   0.3% up N
  RWY 01: REIL. PAPI(P2L)—GA 3.0° TCH 39'. Rgt tfc.
  RWY 19: PAPI(P2L)—GA 3.0° TCH 41'.
RUNWAY DECLARED DISTANCE INFORMATION
  RWY 01:   TORA–5400   TODA–5400   ASDA–5400   LDA–5400
  RWY 05:   TORA–7400   TODA–7400   ASDA–7400   LDA–7400
  RWY 19:   TORA–5400   TODA–5400   ASDA–5400   LDA–5400
  RWY 23:   TORA–7400   TODA–7400   ASDA–7400   LDA–7400
AIRPORT REMARKS: Attended Mon–Fri 1500–0100Z‡. For after hrs
  fuel-self svc avbl or call 208–772–6404, 208–661–4174,
  208–661–7449, 208–699–5433. Self svc fuel avbl with credit
  card. 48 hr PPR for unscheduled ops with more than 30
  passenger seats call arpt manager 208–446–1860. Migratory
  birds on and invof arpt Oct–Nov. Remote cntl airstrip is 2.3 miles
  west AER 05. Arpt conditions avbl on AWOS. Rwy 05 NSTD
  MALSR, thld bar extends 5' byd rwy edge lgts each side. ACTIVATE
  MIRL Rwy 01–19, HIRL Rwy 05–23, REIL Rwy 01 and Rwy 23, MALSR Rwy 05—CTAF. PAPI Rwy 01, Rwy 19, Rwy
  05, and Rwy 23 opr continuously.
WEATHER DATA SOURCES: AWOS–3 135.075 (208) 772–8215.
  HIWAS 108.8 COE.
COMMUNICATIONS: CTAF/UNICOM 122.8
  RCO 122.05 (BOISE RADIO)
Ⓡ **SPOKANE APP/DEP CON** 132.1
AIRSPACE: CLASS E svc continuous.
RADIO AIDS TO NAVIGATION: NOTAM FILE COE.
  (T) VORW/DME 108.8   COE   Chan 25   N47°46.42' W116°49.24'   at fld. 2320/19E.   **HIWAS.**
    DME portion unusable:
      220°–240° byd 15 NM   280°–315° byd 15 NM blo 11,000'.
  POST FALLS NDB (MHW) 347   LEN   N47°44.57' W116°57.66'   053° 6.0 NM to fld.
  ILS 110.7   I–COE   Rwy 05   Class ID.   Localizer unusable 25° left and right of course.

19. (Area 4) The CTAF/UNICOM frequency at Jamestown Airport is
    A. 118.425 MHz.
    B. 122.2 MHz.
    C. 123.0 MHz.

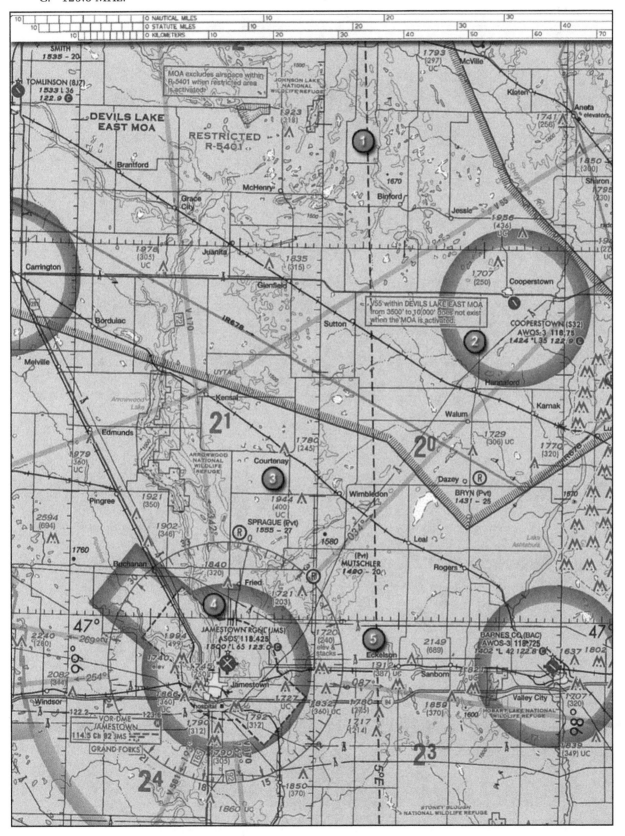

20. (Area 2) What minimum altitude is necessary to vertically clear the obstacle on the southeast side of Winnsboro Airport by 500 feet?

    A. 823 feet MSL.

    B. 1,013 feet MSL.

    C. 1,403 feet MSL.

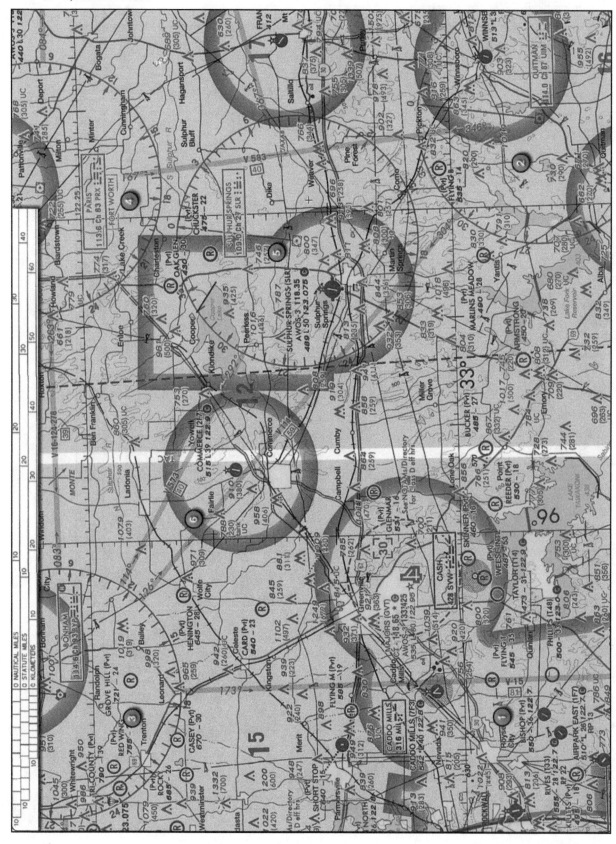

21. Unless otherwise specified, Federal Airways include that Class E airspace extending upward from
    A. 700 feet above the surface up to and including 17,999 feet MSL.
    B. 1,200 feet above the surface up to and including 17,999 feet MSL.
    C. the surface up to and including 18,000 feet MSL.

22. Airspace at an airport with a part-time control tower is classified as Class D airspace only
    A. when the weather minimums are below basic VFR.
    B. when the associated control tower is in operation.
    C. when the associated Flight Service Station is in operation.

23. During operations within controlled airspace at altitudes of less than 1,200 feet AGL, the minimum horizontal distance from clouds requirement for VFR flight is
    A. 1,000 feet.
    B. 1,500 feet.
    C. 2,000 feet.

24. Under what condition may an aircraft operate from a satellite airport within Class C airspace?
    A. The pilot must file a flight plan prior to departure.
    B. The pilot must monitor ATC until clear of the Class C airspace.
    C. The pilot must contact ATC as soon as practicable after takeoff.

25. An ATC radar facility issues the following advisory to a pilot flying on a heading of 360°: "TRAFFIC 10 O'CLOCK, 2 MILES, SOUTHBOUND..." Where should the pilot look for this traffic?
    A. Northwest.
    B. Northeast.
    C. Southwest.

26. When may an emergency locator transmitter (ELT) be tested?
    A. Anytime.
    B. At 15 and 45 minutes past the hour.
    C. During the first 5 minutes after the hour.

27. Every physical process of weather is accompanied by, or is the result of, a
    A. movement of air.
    B. pressure differential.
    C. heat exchange.

28. The presence of ice pellets at the surface is evidence that there
    A. are thunderstorms in the area.
    B. has been cold frontal passage.
    C. is a temperature inversion with freezing rain at a higher altitude.

29. Low-level turbulence can occur and icing can become hazardous in which type of fog?
    A. Rain-induced fog.
    B. Upslope fog.
    C. Steam fog.

30. In which environment is aircraft structural ice most likely to have the highest accumulation rate?
    A. Cumulus clouds with below freezing temperatures.
    B. Freezing drizzle.
    C. Freezing rain.

31. Thunderstorms reach their greatest intensity during the
    A. mature stage.
    B. downdraft stage.
    C. cumulus stage.

END OF COURSE EXAM B

32. For aviation purposes, ceiling is defined as the height above the Earth's surface of the
    A. lowest reported obscuration and the highest layer of clouds reported as overcast.
    B. lowest broken or overcast layer or vertical visibility into an obscuration.
    C. lowest layer of clouds reported as scattered, broken, or thin.

33. What is the valid period for the TAF and KMEM?
    A. 1200Z to 1200Z.
    B. 1200Z to 1800Z.
    C. 1800Z to 1800Z.

TAF

KMEM   121720Z 121818 20012KT 5SM HZ BKN030 PROB40 2022 1SM TSRA OVC008CB
        FM2200 33015G20KT P6SM BKN015 OVC025 PROB40 2202 3SM SHRA
        FM0200 35012KT OVC008 PROB40 0205 2SM-RASN BECMG 0608 02008KT BKN012
        BECMG 1012 00000KT 3SM BR SKC TEMPO 1214 1/2SM FG
        FM1600 VRB06KT P6SM SKC=

KOKC   051130Z 051212 14008KT 5SM BR BKN030 TEMPO 1316 1 1/2SM BR
        FM1600 18010KT P6SM SKC BECMG 2224 20013G20KT 4SM SHRA OVC020
        PROB40 0006 2SM TSRA OVC008CB BECMG 0608 21015KT P6SM SCT040=

---

34. What values are used for Winds Aloft Forecasts?
    A. Magnetic direction and knots.
    B. Magnetic direction and miles per hour.
    C. True direction and knots.

35. How are low-level significant weather (sigwx) prognostic charts best used by a pilot?
    A. For overall planning at all altitudes.
    B. For determining areas to avoid (freezing levels and turbulence).
    C. For analyzing current frontal activity and cloud coverage.

36. What effect does high density altitude have on aircraft performance?
    A. It increases engine performance.
    B. It reduces climb performance.
    C. It increases takeoff performance.

Use the takeoff distance graph to answer Question 37.

37. Determine the approximate total distance required to land over a 50-foot obstacle.

    OAT..90°F

    Pressure altitude............................4,000 feet

    Weight.....................................2,800 pounds

    Headwind component......................10 knots

    A. 1,525 feet
    B. 1,950 feet
    C. 1,775 feet

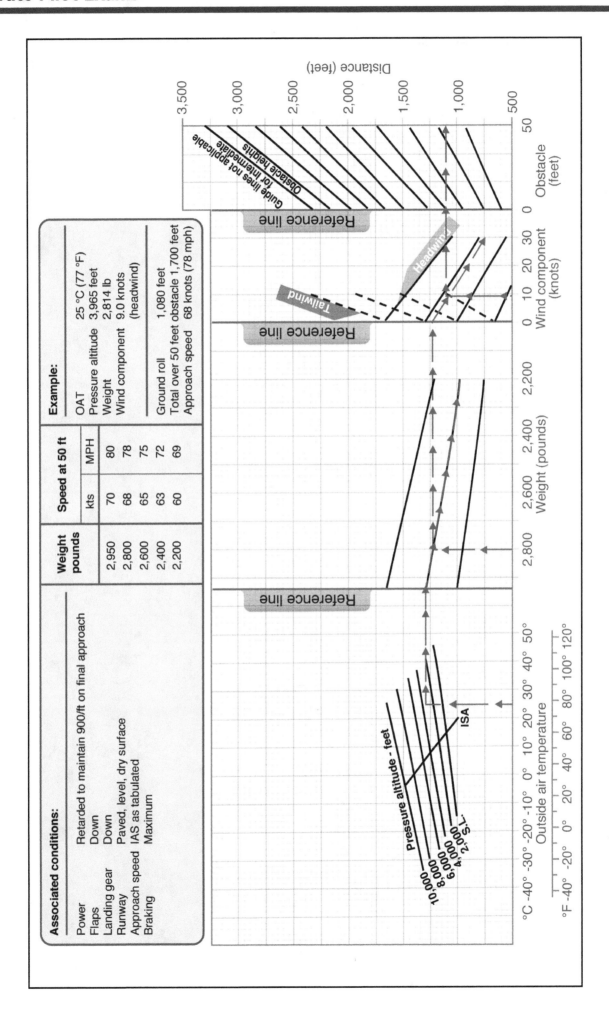

Use the loading graphs to answer Question 38.

38. Calculate the moment of the airplane and determine which category is applicable.

	WEIGHT (LB)	MOM/1000
Empty weight	1,350	51.5
Pilot and Front passenger	310	-----
Rear passengers	96	-----
Fuel, 38 gal	-----	-----
Oil (8 qt)	-----	− 0.2

    A. 79.2, utility category
    B. 80.8, utility category
    C. 81.2, normal category

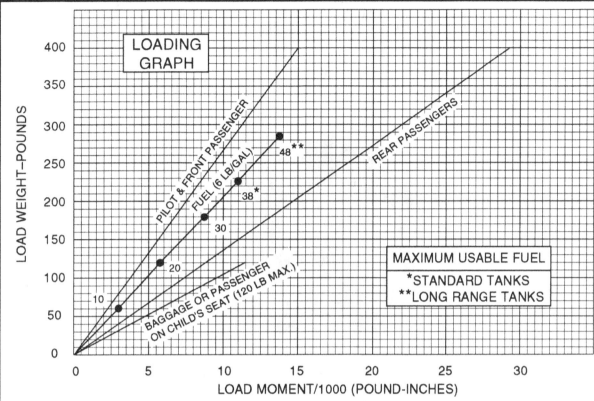

NOTES: (1) Lines representing adjustable seats show the pilot or passenger center of gravity on adjustable seats positioned for an average occupant. Refer to the Loading Arrangements diagram for forward and aft limits of occupant CG range.

(2) Engine Oil: 8 Qt. =15 Lb at –0.2 Moment/1000.

NOTE: The empty weight of this airplane does not include the weight of the oil.

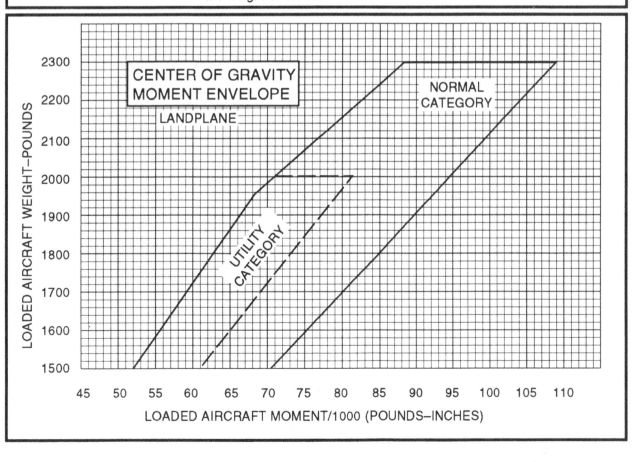

39. How should a VFR flight plan be closed at the completion of the flight at a controlled airport?
    A. The tower automatically closes the flight plan when the airplane turns off the runway.
    B. The pilot must close the flight plan by contacting Flight Service.
    C. The tower relays the instructions to Flight Service when the aircraft contacts the tower for landing

40. The VOR receiver has the indications shown. What radial is the aircraft on?
    A. 300°.
    B. 030°.
    C. 210°.

41. When the course deviation indicator (CDI) needle is centered during an omnireceiver check using a VOR test signal (VOT), the omnibearing selector (OBS) and the TO/FROM indicator should read
    A. 180° FROM, only if the pilot is due north of the VOT.
    B. 0° FROM or 180° TO, regardless of the pilot's position from the VOT.
    C. 0° TO or 180° FROM, regardless of the pilot's position from the VOT.

42. The best method to use when looking for other traffic at night is to
    A. look to the side of the object and scan slowly.
    B. scan the visual field very rapidly.
    C. look to the side of the object and scan rapidly.

43. During a night flight, you observe a steady red light and a flashing red light ahead and at the same altitude. What is the general direction of movement of the other aircraft?
    A. The other aircraft is crossing to the left.
    B. The other aircraft is crossing to the right.
    C. The other aircraft is approaching head-on.

44. VFR approaches to land at night should be accomplished
    A. at a higher airspeed.
    B. with a steeper descent.
    C. the same as during daytime.

45. What is the antidote when a pilot has a hazardous attitude, such as "Macho"?
    A. I can do it.
    B. Taking chances is foolish.
    C. Nothing will happen.

46. What often leads to spatial disorientation or collision with ground/obstacles when flying under Visual Flight Rules (VFR)?
    A. Continual flight into instrument conditions.
    B. Getting behind the aircraft.
    C. Duck-under syndrome.

47. What is the definition of a high-performance airplane?
    A. An airplane with 180 horsepower, or retractable landing gear, flaps, and a fixed-pitch propeller.
    B. An airplane with a normal cruise speed in excess of 200 knots.
    C. An airplane with an engine of more than 200 horsepower.

48. When flying in the airspace underlying Class B airspace, the maximum speed authorized is
    A. 200 knots.
    B. 230 knots.
    C. 250 knots.

49. No person may operate an aircraft in aerobatic flight when
    A. flight visibility is less than 5 miles.
    B. over any congested area of a city, town, or settlement.
    C. less than 2,500 feet AGL.

50. The operator of an aircraft that has been involved in an incident is required to submit a report to the nearest field office of the NTSB
    A. within 7 days.
    B. within 10 days.
    C. when requested.

END OF COURSE EXAM B

END OF COURSE EXAM B

EXAM ANSWER FORM

DATE OF TEST			TEST TITLE OR NO.	TEST GRADE
MONTH	DAY	YEAR		

LAST NAME   **FIRST NAME**

INSTRUCTIONS FOR MARKING THE ANSWER FORM. Completely darken only circle for each. DO NOT USE (X) OR
(✓)Use black lead pencil. To make corrections completely erase incorrect response. Questions are arranged in vertical
sequence as indicated by the arrow.

⬇ 1 (A) (B) (C)   26 (A) (B) (C)   51 (A) (B) (C)   76 (A) (B) (C)

2 (A) (B) (C)   27 (A) (B) (C)   52 (A) (B) (C)   77 (A) (B) (C)

3 (A) (B) (C)   28 (A) (B) (C)   53 (A) (B) (C)   78 (A) (B) (C)

4 (A) (B) (C)   29 (A) (B) (C)   54 (A) (B) (C)   79 (A) (B) (C)

5 (A) (B) (C)   30 (A) (B) (C)   55 (A) (B) (C)   80 (A) (B) (C)

6 (A) (B) (C)   31 (A) (B) (C)   56 (A) (B) (C)   81 (A) (B) (C)

7 (A) (B) (C)   32 (A) (B) (C)   57 (A) (B) (C)   82 (A) (B) (C)

8 (A) (B) (C)   33 (A) (B) (C)   58 (A) (B) (C)   83 (A) (B) (C)

9 (A) (B) (C)   34 (A) (B) (C)   59 (A) (B) (C)   84 (A) (B) (C)

10 (A) (B) (C)   35 (A) (B) (C)   60 (A) (B) (C)   85 (A) (B) (C)

11 (A) (B) (C)   36 (A) (B) (C)   61 (A) (B) (C)   86 (A) (B) (C)

12 (A) (B) (C)   37 (A) (B) (C)   62 (A) (B) (C)   87 (A) (B) (C)

13 (A) (B) (C)   38 (A) (B) (C)   63 (A) (B) (C)   88 (A) (B) (C)

14 (A) (B) (C)   39 (A) (B) (C)   64 (A) (B) (C)   89 (A) (B) (C)

15 (A) (B) (C)   40 (A) (B) (C)   65 (A) (B) (C)   90 (A) (B) (C)

16 (A) (B) (C)   41 (A) (B) (C)   66 (A) (B) (C)   91 (A) (B) (C)

17 (A) (B) (C)   42 (A) (B) (C)   67 (A) (B) (C)   92 (A) (B) (C)

18 (A) (B) (C)   43 (A) (B) (C)   68 (A) (B) (C)   93 (A) (B) (C)

19 (A) (B) (C)   44 (A) (B) (C)   69 (A) (B) (C)   94 (A) (B) (C)

20 (A) (B) (C)   45 (A) (B) (C)   70 (A) (B) (C)   95 (A) (B) (C)

21 (A) (B) (C)   46 (A) (B) (C)   71 (A) (B) (C)   96 (A) (B) (C)

22 (A) (B) (C)   47 (A) (B) (C)   72 (A) (B) (C)   97 (A) (B) (C)

23 (A) (B) (C)   48 (A) (B) (C)   73 (A) (B) (C)   98 (A) (B) (C)

24 (A) (B) (C)   49 (A) (B) (C)   74 (A) (B) (C)   99 (A) (B) (C)

25 (A) (B) (C)   50 (A) (B) (C)   75 (A) (B) (C)   100 (A) (B) (C)

EXAM ANSWER FORM

DATE OF TEST			TEST TITLE OR NO.	TEST GRADE
MONTH	DAY	YEAR		

LAST NAME   FIRST NAME

INSTRUCTIONS FOR MARKING THE ANSWER FORM. Completely darken only circle for each. DO NOT USE (X) OR
(✓)Use black lead pencil. To make corrections completely erase incorrect response. Questions are arranged in vertical
sequence as indicated by the arrow.

1	Ⓐ Ⓑ Ⓒ	26	Ⓐ Ⓑ Ⓒ	51	Ⓐ Ⓑ Ⓒ	76	Ⓐ Ⓑ Ⓒ
2	Ⓐ Ⓑ Ⓒ	27	Ⓐ Ⓑ Ⓒ	52	Ⓐ Ⓑ Ⓒ	77	Ⓐ Ⓑ Ⓒ
3	Ⓐ Ⓑ Ⓒ	28	Ⓐ Ⓑ Ⓒ	53	Ⓐ Ⓑ Ⓒ	78	Ⓐ Ⓑ Ⓒ
4	Ⓐ Ⓑ Ⓒ	29	Ⓐ Ⓑ Ⓒ	54	Ⓐ Ⓑ Ⓒ	79	Ⓐ Ⓑ Ⓒ
5	Ⓐ Ⓑ Ⓒ	30	Ⓐ Ⓑ Ⓒ	55	Ⓐ Ⓑ Ⓒ	80	Ⓐ Ⓑ Ⓒ
6	Ⓐ Ⓑ Ⓒ	31	Ⓐ Ⓑ Ⓒ	56	Ⓐ Ⓑ Ⓒ	81	Ⓐ Ⓑ Ⓒ
7	Ⓐ Ⓑ Ⓒ	32	Ⓐ Ⓑ Ⓒ	57	Ⓐ Ⓑ Ⓒ	82	Ⓐ Ⓑ Ⓒ
8	Ⓐ Ⓑ Ⓒ	33	Ⓐ Ⓑ Ⓒ	58	Ⓐ Ⓑ Ⓒ	83	Ⓐ Ⓑ Ⓒ
9	Ⓐ Ⓑ Ⓒ	34	Ⓐ Ⓑ Ⓒ	59	Ⓐ Ⓑ Ⓒ	84	Ⓐ Ⓑ Ⓒ
10	Ⓐ Ⓑ Ⓒ	35	Ⓐ Ⓑ Ⓒ	60	Ⓐ Ⓑ Ⓒ	85	Ⓐ Ⓑ Ⓒ
11	Ⓐ Ⓑ Ⓒ	36	Ⓐ Ⓑ Ⓒ	61	Ⓐ Ⓑ Ⓒ	86	Ⓐ Ⓑ Ⓒ
12	Ⓐ Ⓑ Ⓒ	37	Ⓐ Ⓑ Ⓒ	62	Ⓐ Ⓑ Ⓒ	87	Ⓐ Ⓑ Ⓒ
13	Ⓐ Ⓑ Ⓒ	38	Ⓐ Ⓑ Ⓒ	63	Ⓐ Ⓑ Ⓒ	88	Ⓐ Ⓑ Ⓒ
14	Ⓐ Ⓑ Ⓒ	39	Ⓐ Ⓑ Ⓒ	64	Ⓐ Ⓑ Ⓒ	89	Ⓐ Ⓑ Ⓒ
15	Ⓐ Ⓑ Ⓒ	40	Ⓐ Ⓑ Ⓒ	65	Ⓐ Ⓑ Ⓒ	90	Ⓐ Ⓑ Ⓒ
16	Ⓐ Ⓑ Ⓒ	41	Ⓐ Ⓑ Ⓒ	66	Ⓐ Ⓑ Ⓒ	91	Ⓐ Ⓑ Ⓒ
17	Ⓐ Ⓑ Ⓒ	42	Ⓐ Ⓑ Ⓒ	67	Ⓐ Ⓑ Ⓒ	92	Ⓐ Ⓑ Ⓒ
18	Ⓐ Ⓑ Ⓒ	43	Ⓐ Ⓑ Ⓒ	68	Ⓐ Ⓑ Ⓒ	93	Ⓐ Ⓑ Ⓒ
19	Ⓐ Ⓑ Ⓒ	44	Ⓐ Ⓑ Ⓒ	69	Ⓐ Ⓑ Ⓒ	94	Ⓐ Ⓑ Ⓒ
20	Ⓐ Ⓑ Ⓒ	45	Ⓐ Ⓑ Ⓒ	70	Ⓐ Ⓑ Ⓒ	95	Ⓐ Ⓑ Ⓒ
21	Ⓐ Ⓑ Ⓒ	46	Ⓐ Ⓑ Ⓒ	71	Ⓐ Ⓑ Ⓒ	96	Ⓐ Ⓑ Ⓒ
22	Ⓐ Ⓑ Ⓒ	47	Ⓐ Ⓑ Ⓒ	72	Ⓐ Ⓑ Ⓒ	97	Ⓐ Ⓑ Ⓒ
23	Ⓐ Ⓑ Ⓒ	48	Ⓐ Ⓑ Ⓒ	73	Ⓐ Ⓑ Ⓒ	98	Ⓐ Ⓑ Ⓒ
24	Ⓐ Ⓑ Ⓒ	49	Ⓐ Ⓑ Ⓒ	74	Ⓐ Ⓑ Ⓒ	99	Ⓐ Ⓑ Ⓒ
25	Ⓐ Ⓑ Ⓒ	50	Ⓐ Ⓑ Ⓒ	75	Ⓐ Ⓑ Ⓒ	100	Ⓐ Ⓑ Ⓒ

EXAM ANSWER FORM

	DATE OF TEST			TEST TITLE OR NO.	TEST GRADE
MONTH	DAY	YEAR			

LAST NAME **FIRST NAME**

INSTRUCTIONS FOR MARKING THE ANSWER FORM. Completely darken only circle for each. DO NOT USE (X) OR
(✓)Use black lead pencil. To make corrections completely erase incorrect response. Questions are arranged in vertical
sequence as indicated by the arrow.

1 Ⓐ Ⓑ Ⓒ   26 Ⓐ Ⓑ Ⓒ   51 Ⓐ Ⓑ Ⓒ   76 Ⓐ Ⓑ Ⓒ
2 Ⓐ Ⓑ Ⓒ   27 Ⓐ Ⓑ Ⓒ   52 Ⓐ Ⓑ Ⓒ   77 Ⓐ Ⓑ Ⓒ
3 Ⓐ Ⓑ Ⓒ   28 Ⓐ Ⓑ Ⓒ   53 Ⓐ Ⓑ Ⓒ   78 Ⓐ Ⓑ Ⓒ
4 Ⓐ Ⓑ Ⓒ   29 Ⓐ Ⓑ Ⓒ   54 Ⓐ Ⓑ Ⓒ   79 Ⓐ Ⓑ Ⓒ
5 Ⓐ Ⓑ Ⓒ   30 Ⓐ Ⓑ Ⓒ   55 Ⓐ Ⓑ Ⓒ   80 Ⓐ Ⓑ Ⓒ
6 Ⓐ Ⓑ Ⓒ   31 Ⓐ Ⓑ Ⓒ   56 Ⓐ Ⓑ Ⓒ   81 Ⓐ Ⓑ Ⓒ
7 Ⓐ Ⓑ Ⓒ   32 Ⓐ Ⓑ Ⓒ   57 Ⓐ Ⓑ Ⓒ   82 Ⓐ Ⓑ Ⓒ
8 Ⓐ Ⓑ Ⓒ   33 Ⓐ Ⓑ Ⓒ   58 Ⓐ Ⓑ Ⓒ   83 Ⓐ Ⓑ Ⓒ
9 Ⓐ Ⓑ Ⓒ   34 Ⓐ Ⓑ Ⓒ   59 Ⓐ Ⓑ Ⓒ   84 Ⓐ Ⓑ Ⓒ
10 Ⓐ Ⓑ Ⓒ   35 Ⓐ Ⓑ Ⓒ   60 Ⓐ Ⓑ Ⓒ   85 Ⓐ Ⓑ Ⓒ
11 Ⓐ Ⓑ Ⓒ   36 Ⓐ Ⓑ Ⓒ   61 Ⓐ Ⓑ Ⓒ   86 Ⓐ Ⓑ Ⓒ
12 Ⓐ Ⓑ Ⓒ   37 Ⓐ Ⓑ Ⓒ   62 Ⓐ Ⓑ Ⓒ   87 Ⓐ Ⓑ Ⓒ
13 Ⓐ Ⓑ Ⓒ   38 Ⓐ Ⓑ Ⓒ   63 Ⓐ Ⓑ Ⓒ   88 Ⓐ Ⓑ Ⓒ
14 Ⓐ Ⓑ Ⓒ   39 Ⓐ Ⓑ Ⓒ   64 Ⓐ Ⓑ Ⓒ   89 Ⓐ Ⓑ Ⓒ
15 Ⓐ Ⓑ Ⓒ   40 Ⓐ Ⓑ Ⓒ   65 Ⓐ Ⓑ Ⓒ   90 Ⓐ Ⓑ Ⓒ
16 Ⓐ Ⓑ Ⓒ   41 Ⓐ Ⓑ Ⓒ   66 Ⓐ Ⓑ Ⓒ   91 Ⓐ Ⓑ Ⓒ
17 Ⓐ Ⓑ Ⓒ   42 Ⓐ Ⓑ Ⓒ   67 Ⓐ Ⓑ Ⓒ   92 Ⓐ Ⓑ Ⓒ
18 Ⓐ Ⓑ Ⓒ   43 Ⓐ Ⓑ Ⓒ   68 Ⓐ Ⓑ Ⓒ   93 Ⓐ Ⓑ Ⓒ
19 Ⓐ Ⓑ Ⓒ   44 Ⓐ Ⓑ Ⓒ   69 Ⓐ Ⓑ Ⓒ   94 Ⓐ Ⓑ Ⓒ
20 Ⓐ Ⓑ Ⓒ   45 Ⓐ Ⓑ Ⓒ   70 Ⓐ Ⓑ Ⓒ   95 Ⓐ Ⓑ Ⓒ
21 Ⓐ Ⓑ Ⓒ   46 Ⓐ Ⓑ Ⓒ   71 Ⓐ Ⓑ Ⓒ   96 Ⓐ Ⓑ Ⓒ
22 Ⓐ Ⓑ Ⓒ   47 Ⓐ Ⓑ Ⓒ   72 Ⓐ Ⓑ Ⓒ   97 Ⓐ Ⓑ Ⓒ
23 Ⓐ Ⓑ Ⓒ   48 Ⓐ Ⓑ Ⓒ   73 Ⓐ Ⓑ Ⓒ   98 Ⓐ Ⓑ Ⓒ
24 Ⓐ Ⓑ Ⓒ   49 Ⓐ Ⓑ Ⓒ   74 Ⓐ Ⓑ Ⓒ   99 Ⓐ Ⓑ Ⓒ
25 Ⓐ Ⓑ Ⓒ   50 Ⓐ Ⓑ Ⓒ   75 Ⓐ Ⓑ Ⓒ   100 Ⓐ Ⓑ Ⓒ

EXAM ANSWER FORM

DATE OF TEST			TEST TITLE OR NO.	TEST GRADE
MONTH	DAY	YEAR		

LAST NAME   **FIRST NAME**

INSTRUCTIONS FOR MARKING THE ANSWER FORM. Completely darken only circle for each. DO NOT USE (X) OR (✓)Use black lead pencil. To make corrections completely erase incorrect response. Questions are arranged in vertical sequence as indicated by the arrow.

⬇

1 Ⓐ Ⓑ Ⓒ	26 Ⓐ Ⓑ Ⓒ	51 Ⓐ Ⓑ Ⓒ	76 Ⓐ Ⓑ Ⓒ
2 Ⓐ Ⓑ Ⓒ	27 Ⓐ Ⓑ Ⓒ	52 Ⓐ Ⓑ Ⓒ	77 Ⓐ Ⓑ Ⓒ
3 Ⓐ Ⓑ Ⓒ	28 Ⓐ Ⓑ Ⓒ	53 Ⓐ Ⓑ Ⓒ	78 Ⓐ Ⓑ Ⓒ
4 Ⓐ Ⓑ Ⓒ	29 Ⓐ Ⓑ Ⓒ	54 Ⓐ Ⓑ Ⓒ	79 Ⓐ Ⓑ Ⓒ
5 Ⓐ Ⓑ Ⓒ	30 Ⓐ Ⓑ Ⓒ	55 Ⓐ Ⓑ Ⓒ	80 Ⓐ Ⓑ Ⓒ
6 Ⓐ Ⓑ Ⓒ	31 Ⓐ Ⓑ Ⓒ	56 Ⓐ Ⓑ Ⓒ	81 Ⓐ Ⓑ Ⓒ
7 Ⓐ Ⓑ Ⓒ	32 Ⓐ Ⓑ Ⓒ	57 Ⓐ Ⓑ Ⓒ	82 Ⓐ Ⓑ Ⓒ
8 Ⓐ Ⓑ Ⓒ	33 Ⓐ Ⓑ Ⓒ	58 Ⓐ Ⓑ Ⓒ	83 Ⓐ Ⓑ Ⓒ
9 Ⓐ Ⓑ Ⓒ	34 Ⓐ Ⓑ Ⓒ	59 Ⓐ Ⓑ Ⓒ	84 Ⓐ Ⓑ Ⓒ
10 Ⓐ Ⓑ Ⓒ	35 Ⓐ Ⓑ Ⓒ	60 Ⓐ Ⓑ Ⓒ	85 Ⓐ Ⓑ Ⓒ
11 Ⓐ Ⓑ Ⓒ	36 Ⓐ Ⓑ Ⓒ	61 Ⓐ Ⓑ Ⓒ	86 Ⓐ Ⓑ Ⓒ
12 Ⓐ Ⓑ Ⓒ	37 Ⓐ Ⓑ Ⓒ	62 Ⓐ Ⓑ Ⓒ	87 Ⓐ Ⓑ Ⓒ
13 Ⓐ Ⓑ Ⓒ	38 Ⓐ Ⓑ Ⓒ	63 Ⓐ Ⓑ Ⓒ	88 Ⓐ Ⓑ Ⓒ
14 Ⓐ Ⓑ Ⓒ	39 Ⓐ Ⓑ Ⓒ	64 Ⓐ Ⓑ Ⓒ	89 Ⓐ Ⓑ Ⓒ
15 Ⓐ Ⓑ Ⓒ	40 Ⓐ Ⓑ Ⓒ	65 Ⓐ Ⓑ Ⓒ	90 Ⓐ Ⓑ Ⓒ
16 Ⓐ Ⓑ Ⓒ	41 Ⓐ Ⓑ Ⓒ	66 Ⓐ Ⓑ Ⓒ	91 Ⓐ Ⓑ Ⓒ
17 Ⓐ Ⓑ Ⓒ	42 Ⓐ Ⓑ Ⓒ	67 Ⓐ Ⓑ Ⓒ	92 Ⓐ Ⓑ Ⓒ
18 Ⓐ Ⓑ Ⓒ	43 Ⓐ Ⓑ Ⓒ	68 Ⓐ Ⓑ Ⓒ	93 Ⓐ Ⓑ Ⓒ
19 Ⓐ Ⓑ Ⓒ	44 Ⓐ Ⓑ Ⓒ	69 Ⓐ Ⓑ Ⓒ	94 Ⓐ Ⓑ Ⓒ
20 Ⓐ Ⓑ Ⓒ	45 Ⓐ Ⓑ Ⓒ	70 Ⓐ Ⓑ Ⓒ	95 Ⓐ Ⓑ Ⓒ
21 Ⓐ Ⓑ Ⓒ	46 Ⓐ Ⓑ Ⓒ	71 Ⓐ Ⓑ Ⓒ	96 Ⓐ Ⓑ Ⓒ
22 Ⓐ Ⓑ Ⓒ	47 Ⓐ Ⓑ Ⓒ	72 Ⓐ Ⓑ Ⓒ	97 Ⓐ Ⓑ Ⓒ
23 Ⓐ Ⓑ Ⓒ	48 Ⓐ Ⓑ Ⓒ	73 Ⓐ Ⓑ Ⓒ	98 Ⓐ Ⓑ Ⓒ
24 Ⓐ Ⓑ Ⓒ	49 Ⓐ Ⓑ Ⓒ	74 Ⓐ Ⓑ Ⓒ	99 Ⓐ Ⓑ Ⓒ
25 Ⓐ Ⓑ Ⓒ	50 Ⓐ Ⓑ Ⓒ	75 Ⓐ Ⓑ Ⓒ	100 Ⓐ Ⓑ Ⓒ

EXAM ANSWER FORM

DATE OF TEST			TEST TITLE OR NO.	TEST GRADE
MONTH	DAY	YEAR		

LAST NAME   FIRST NAME

INSTRUCTIONS FOR MARKING THE ANSWER FORM. Completely darken only circle for each. DO NOT USE (X) OR
(✓)Use black lead pencil. To make corrections completely erase incorrect response. Questions are arranged in vertical
sequence as indicated by the arrow.

1 Ⓐ Ⓑ Ⓒ	26 Ⓐ Ⓑ Ⓒ	51 Ⓐ Ⓑ Ⓒ	76 Ⓐ Ⓑ Ⓒ
2 Ⓐ Ⓑ Ⓒ	27 Ⓐ Ⓑ Ⓒ	52 Ⓐ Ⓑ Ⓒ	77 Ⓐ Ⓑ Ⓒ
3 Ⓐ Ⓑ Ⓒ	28 Ⓐ Ⓑ Ⓒ	53 Ⓐ Ⓑ Ⓒ	78 Ⓐ Ⓑ Ⓒ
4 Ⓐ Ⓑ Ⓒ	29 Ⓐ Ⓑ Ⓒ	54 Ⓐ Ⓑ Ⓒ	79 Ⓐ Ⓑ Ⓒ
5 Ⓐ Ⓑ Ⓒ	30 Ⓐ Ⓑ Ⓒ	55 Ⓐ Ⓑ Ⓒ	80 Ⓐ Ⓑ Ⓒ
6 Ⓐ Ⓑ Ⓒ	31 Ⓐ Ⓑ Ⓒ	56 Ⓐ Ⓑ Ⓒ	81 Ⓐ Ⓑ Ⓒ
7 Ⓐ Ⓑ Ⓒ	32 Ⓐ Ⓑ Ⓒ	57 Ⓐ Ⓑ Ⓒ	82 Ⓐ Ⓑ Ⓒ
8 Ⓐ Ⓑ Ⓒ	33 Ⓐ Ⓑ Ⓒ	58 Ⓐ Ⓑ Ⓒ	83 Ⓐ Ⓑ Ⓒ
9 Ⓐ Ⓑ Ⓒ	34 Ⓐ Ⓑ Ⓒ	59 Ⓐ Ⓑ Ⓒ	84 Ⓐ Ⓑ Ⓒ
10 Ⓐ Ⓑ Ⓒ	35 Ⓐ Ⓑ Ⓒ	60 Ⓐ Ⓑ Ⓒ	85 Ⓐ Ⓑ Ⓒ
11 Ⓐ Ⓑ Ⓒ	36 Ⓐ Ⓑ Ⓒ	61 Ⓐ Ⓑ Ⓒ	86 Ⓐ Ⓑ Ⓒ
12 Ⓐ Ⓑ Ⓒ	37 Ⓐ Ⓑ Ⓒ	62 Ⓐ Ⓑ Ⓒ	87 Ⓐ Ⓑ Ⓒ
13 Ⓐ Ⓑ Ⓒ	38 Ⓐ Ⓑ Ⓒ	63 Ⓐ Ⓑ Ⓒ	88 Ⓐ Ⓑ Ⓒ
14 Ⓐ Ⓑ Ⓒ	39 Ⓐ Ⓑ Ⓒ	64 Ⓐ Ⓑ Ⓒ	89 Ⓐ Ⓑ Ⓒ
15 Ⓐ Ⓑ Ⓒ	40 Ⓐ Ⓑ Ⓒ	65 Ⓐ Ⓑ Ⓒ	90 Ⓐ Ⓑ Ⓒ
16 Ⓐ Ⓑ Ⓒ	41 Ⓐ Ⓑ Ⓒ	66 Ⓐ Ⓑ Ⓒ	91 Ⓐ Ⓑ Ⓒ
17 Ⓐ Ⓑ Ⓒ	42 Ⓐ Ⓑ Ⓒ	67 Ⓐ Ⓑ Ⓒ	92 Ⓐ Ⓑ Ⓒ
18 Ⓐ Ⓑ Ⓒ	43 Ⓐ Ⓑ Ⓒ	68 Ⓐ Ⓑ Ⓒ	93 Ⓐ Ⓑ Ⓒ
19 Ⓐ Ⓑ Ⓒ	44 Ⓐ Ⓑ Ⓒ	69 Ⓐ Ⓑ Ⓒ	94 Ⓐ Ⓑ Ⓒ
20 Ⓐ Ⓑ Ⓒ	45 Ⓐ Ⓑ Ⓒ	70 Ⓐ Ⓑ Ⓒ	95 Ⓐ Ⓑ Ⓒ
21 Ⓐ Ⓑ Ⓒ	46 Ⓐ Ⓑ Ⓒ	71 Ⓐ Ⓑ Ⓒ	96 Ⓐ Ⓑ Ⓒ
22 Ⓐ Ⓑ Ⓒ	47 Ⓐ Ⓑ Ⓒ	72 Ⓐ Ⓑ Ⓒ	97 Ⓐ Ⓑ Ⓒ
23 Ⓐ Ⓑ Ⓒ	48 Ⓐ Ⓑ Ⓒ	73 Ⓐ Ⓑ Ⓒ	98 Ⓐ Ⓑ Ⓒ
24 Ⓐ Ⓑ Ⓒ	49 Ⓐ Ⓑ Ⓒ	74 Ⓐ Ⓑ Ⓒ	99 Ⓐ Ⓑ Ⓒ
25 Ⓐ Ⓑ Ⓒ	50 Ⓐ Ⓑ Ⓒ	75 Ⓐ Ⓑ Ⓒ	100 Ⓐ Ⓑ Ⓒ

EXAM ANSWER FORM

DATE OF TEST			TEST TITLE OR NO.	TEST GRADE
MONTH	DAY	YEAR		

LAST NAME   **FIRST NAME**

**INSTRUCTIONS FOR MARKING THE ANSWER FORM. Completely darken only circle for each. DO NOT USE (X) OR
(✓)Use black lead pencil. To make corrections completely erase incorrect response. Questions are arranged in vertical
sequence as indicated by the arrow.**

1	Ⓐ Ⓑ Ⓒ	26	Ⓐ Ⓑ Ⓒ	51	Ⓐ Ⓑ Ⓒ	76	Ⓐ Ⓑ Ⓒ
2	Ⓐ Ⓑ Ⓒ	27	Ⓐ Ⓑ Ⓒ	52	Ⓐ Ⓑ Ⓒ	77	Ⓐ Ⓑ Ⓒ
3	Ⓐ Ⓑ Ⓒ	28	Ⓐ Ⓑ Ⓒ	53	Ⓐ Ⓑ Ⓒ	78	Ⓐ Ⓑ Ⓒ
4	Ⓐ Ⓑ Ⓒ	29	Ⓐ Ⓑ Ⓒ	54	Ⓐ Ⓑ Ⓒ	79	Ⓐ Ⓑ Ⓒ
5	Ⓐ Ⓑ Ⓒ	30	Ⓐ Ⓑ Ⓒ	55	Ⓐ Ⓑ Ⓒ	80	Ⓐ Ⓑ Ⓒ
6	Ⓐ Ⓑ Ⓒ	31	Ⓐ Ⓑ Ⓒ	56	Ⓐ Ⓑ Ⓒ	81	Ⓐ Ⓑ Ⓒ
7	Ⓐ Ⓑ Ⓒ	32	Ⓐ Ⓑ Ⓒ	57	Ⓐ Ⓑ Ⓒ	82	Ⓐ Ⓑ Ⓒ
8	Ⓐ Ⓑ Ⓒ	33	Ⓐ Ⓑ Ⓒ	58	Ⓐ Ⓑ Ⓒ	83	Ⓐ Ⓑ Ⓒ
9	Ⓐ Ⓑ Ⓒ	34	Ⓐ Ⓑ Ⓒ	59	Ⓐ Ⓑ Ⓒ	84	Ⓐ Ⓑ Ⓒ
10	Ⓐ Ⓑ Ⓒ	35	Ⓐ Ⓑ Ⓒ	60	Ⓐ Ⓑ Ⓒ	85	Ⓐ Ⓑ Ⓒ
11	Ⓐ Ⓑ Ⓒ	36	Ⓐ Ⓑ Ⓒ	61	Ⓐ Ⓑ Ⓒ	86	Ⓐ Ⓑ Ⓒ
12	Ⓐ Ⓑ Ⓒ	37	Ⓐ Ⓑ Ⓒ	62	Ⓐ Ⓑ Ⓒ	87	Ⓐ Ⓑ Ⓒ
13	Ⓐ Ⓑ Ⓒ	38	Ⓐ Ⓑ Ⓒ	63	Ⓐ Ⓑ Ⓒ	88	Ⓐ Ⓑ Ⓒ
14	Ⓐ Ⓑ Ⓒ	39	Ⓐ Ⓑ Ⓒ	64	Ⓐ Ⓑ Ⓒ	89	Ⓐ Ⓑ Ⓒ
15	Ⓐ Ⓑ Ⓒ	40	Ⓐ Ⓑ Ⓒ	65	Ⓐ Ⓑ Ⓒ	90	Ⓐ Ⓑ Ⓒ
16	Ⓐ Ⓑ Ⓒ	41	Ⓐ Ⓑ Ⓒ	66	Ⓐ Ⓑ Ⓒ	91	Ⓐ Ⓑ Ⓒ
17	Ⓐ Ⓑ Ⓒ	42	Ⓐ Ⓑ Ⓒ	67	Ⓐ Ⓑ Ⓒ	92	Ⓐ Ⓑ Ⓒ
18	Ⓐ Ⓑ Ⓒ	43	Ⓐ Ⓑ Ⓒ	68	Ⓐ Ⓑ Ⓒ	93	Ⓐ Ⓑ Ⓒ
19	Ⓐ Ⓑ Ⓒ	44	Ⓐ Ⓑ Ⓒ	69	Ⓐ Ⓑ Ⓒ	94	Ⓐ Ⓑ Ⓒ
20	Ⓐ Ⓑ Ⓒ	45	Ⓐ Ⓑ Ⓒ	70	Ⓐ Ⓑ Ⓒ	95	Ⓐ Ⓑ Ⓒ
21	Ⓐ Ⓑ Ⓒ	46	Ⓐ Ⓑ Ⓒ	71	Ⓐ Ⓑ Ⓒ	96	Ⓐ Ⓑ Ⓒ
22	Ⓐ Ⓑ Ⓒ	47	Ⓐ Ⓑ Ⓒ	72	Ⓐ Ⓑ Ⓒ	97	Ⓐ Ⓑ Ⓒ
23	Ⓐ Ⓑ Ⓒ	48	Ⓐ Ⓑ Ⓒ	73	Ⓐ Ⓑ Ⓒ	98	Ⓐ Ⓑ Ⓒ
24	Ⓐ Ⓑ Ⓒ	49	Ⓐ Ⓑ Ⓒ	74	Ⓐ Ⓑ Ⓒ	99	Ⓐ Ⓑ Ⓒ
25	Ⓐ Ⓑ Ⓒ	50	Ⓐ Ⓑ Ⓒ	75	Ⓐ Ⓑ Ⓒ	100	Ⓐ Ⓑ Ⓒ

EXAM ANSWER FORM

DATE OF TEST			TEST TITLE OR NO.	TEST GRADE
MONTH	DAY	YEAR		

LAST NAME   **FIRST NAME**

INSTRUCTIONS FOR MARKING THE ANSWER FORM. Completely darken only circle for each. DO NOT USE (X) OR (✓)Use black lead pencil. To make corrections completely erase incorrect response. Questions are arranged in vertical sequence as indicated by the arrow.

1	Ⓐ	Ⓑ	Ⓒ	26	Ⓐ	Ⓑ	Ⓒ	51	Ⓐ	Ⓑ	Ⓒ	76	Ⓐ	Ⓑ	Ⓒ
2	Ⓐ	Ⓑ	Ⓒ	27	Ⓐ	Ⓑ	Ⓒ	52	Ⓐ	Ⓑ	Ⓒ	77	Ⓐ	Ⓑ	Ⓒ
3	Ⓐ	Ⓑ	Ⓒ	28	Ⓐ	Ⓑ	Ⓒ	53	Ⓐ	Ⓑ	Ⓒ	78	Ⓐ	Ⓑ	Ⓒ
4	Ⓐ	Ⓑ	Ⓒ	29	Ⓐ	Ⓑ	Ⓒ	54	Ⓐ	Ⓑ	Ⓒ	79	Ⓐ	Ⓑ	Ⓒ
5	Ⓐ	Ⓑ	Ⓒ	30	Ⓐ	Ⓑ	Ⓒ	55	Ⓐ	Ⓑ	Ⓒ	80	Ⓐ	Ⓑ	Ⓒ
6	Ⓐ	Ⓑ	Ⓒ	31	Ⓐ	Ⓑ	Ⓒ	56	Ⓐ	Ⓑ	Ⓒ	81	Ⓐ	Ⓑ	Ⓒ
7	Ⓐ	Ⓑ	Ⓒ	32	Ⓐ	Ⓑ	Ⓒ	57	Ⓐ	Ⓑ	Ⓒ	82	Ⓐ	Ⓑ	Ⓒ
8	Ⓐ	Ⓑ	Ⓒ	33	Ⓐ	Ⓑ	Ⓒ	58	Ⓐ	Ⓑ	Ⓒ	83	Ⓐ	Ⓑ	Ⓒ
9	Ⓐ	Ⓑ	Ⓒ	34	Ⓐ	Ⓑ	Ⓒ	59	Ⓐ	Ⓑ	Ⓒ	84	Ⓐ	Ⓑ	Ⓒ
10	Ⓐ	Ⓑ	Ⓒ	35	Ⓐ	Ⓑ	Ⓒ	60	Ⓐ	Ⓑ	Ⓒ	85	Ⓐ	Ⓑ	Ⓒ
11	Ⓐ	Ⓑ	Ⓒ	36	Ⓐ	Ⓑ	Ⓒ	61	Ⓐ	Ⓑ	Ⓒ	86	Ⓐ	Ⓑ	Ⓒ
12	Ⓐ	Ⓑ	Ⓒ	37	Ⓐ	Ⓑ	Ⓒ	62	Ⓐ	Ⓑ	Ⓒ	87	Ⓐ	Ⓑ	Ⓒ
13	Ⓐ	Ⓑ	Ⓒ	38	Ⓐ	Ⓑ	Ⓒ	63	Ⓐ	Ⓑ	Ⓒ	88	Ⓐ	Ⓑ	Ⓒ
14	Ⓐ	Ⓑ	Ⓒ	39	Ⓐ	Ⓑ	Ⓒ	64	Ⓐ	Ⓑ	Ⓒ	89	Ⓐ	Ⓑ	Ⓒ
15	Ⓐ	Ⓑ	Ⓒ	40	Ⓐ	Ⓑ	Ⓒ	65	Ⓐ	Ⓑ	Ⓒ	90	Ⓐ	Ⓑ	Ⓒ
16	Ⓐ	Ⓑ	Ⓒ	41	Ⓐ	Ⓑ	Ⓒ	66	Ⓐ	Ⓑ	Ⓒ	91	Ⓐ	Ⓑ	Ⓒ
17	Ⓐ	Ⓑ	Ⓒ	42	Ⓐ	Ⓑ	Ⓒ	67	Ⓐ	Ⓑ	Ⓒ	92	Ⓐ	Ⓑ	Ⓒ
18	Ⓐ	Ⓑ	Ⓒ	43	Ⓐ	Ⓑ	Ⓒ	68	Ⓐ	Ⓑ	Ⓒ	93	Ⓐ	Ⓑ	Ⓒ
19	Ⓐ	Ⓑ	Ⓒ	44	Ⓐ	Ⓑ	Ⓒ	69	Ⓐ	Ⓑ	Ⓒ	94	Ⓐ	Ⓑ	Ⓒ
20	Ⓐ	Ⓑ	Ⓒ	45	Ⓐ	Ⓑ	Ⓒ	70	Ⓐ	Ⓑ	Ⓒ	95	Ⓐ	Ⓑ	Ⓒ
21	Ⓐ	Ⓑ	Ⓒ	46	Ⓐ	Ⓑ	Ⓒ	71	Ⓐ	Ⓑ	Ⓒ	96	Ⓐ	Ⓑ	Ⓒ
22	Ⓐ	Ⓑ	Ⓒ	47	Ⓐ	Ⓑ	Ⓒ	72	Ⓐ	Ⓑ	Ⓒ	97	Ⓐ	Ⓑ	Ⓒ
23	Ⓐ	Ⓑ	Ⓒ	48	Ⓐ	Ⓑ	Ⓒ	73	Ⓐ	Ⓑ	Ⓒ	98	Ⓐ	Ⓑ	Ⓒ
24	Ⓐ	Ⓑ	Ⓒ	49	Ⓐ	Ⓑ	Ⓒ	74	Ⓐ	Ⓑ	Ⓒ	99	Ⓐ	Ⓑ	Ⓒ
25	Ⓐ	Ⓑ	Ⓒ	50	Ⓐ	Ⓑ	Ⓒ	75	Ⓐ	Ⓑ	Ⓒ	100	Ⓐ	Ⓑ	Ⓒ